D1201919

American Art of the 20's and 30's

Paintings by Nineteen Living Americans

with a foreword by Alfred H. Barr, Jr.

Painting and Sculpture by Living Americans

with a foreword by Alfred H. Barr, Jr.

Murals by American Painters and Photographers

by Lincoln Kirstein and Julien Levy

The Museum of Modern Art, New York
Reprint Edition, 1969
Published for The Museum of Modern Art by Arno Press

Reprint Edition, 1969 Arno Press
Library of Congress Catalog Card No. 76-86439

PAINTINGS BY NINETEEN LIVING AMERICANS

DECEMBER 13 · 1929 TO JANUARY 12 · 1930

THE MUSEUM OF MODERN ART
NEW YORK

CONTENTS

ACKNOWLEDGMENTS

The exhibition has been selected from the following collections

MR. WILLIAM RUSSELL ALLEN, BOSTON

MR. JERE ABBOTT, NEW YORK

MRS. JOHN O. BLANCHARD, NEW YORK

MISS L. P. BLISS, NEW YORK

MR. STEPHEN C. CLARK, NEW YORK

MR. FRANK CROWNINSHIELD, NEW YORK

MRS. G. WARRINGTON CURTIS, NEW YORK

MR. CHARLES DANIEL, NEW YORK

THE DOWNTOWN GALLERY, NEW YORK

MR. A. E. GALLATIN, NEW YORK

MR. A. CONGER GOODYEAR, NEW YORK

PROF. CLIFTON R. HALL, PRINCETON, NEW JERSEY

DR. AND MRS. F. H. HIRSCHLAND, NEW YORK

MR. FERDINAND HOWALD, COLUMBUS, OHIO

MRS. EDWARD A. JORDAN, NEW YORK

THE KRAUSHAAR GALLERY, NEW YORK

MR. ADOLPH LEWISOHN, NEW YORK

MR. AND MRS. SAMUEL A. LEWISOHN, NEW YORK

MR. AND MRS. CHARLES LIEBMAN, NEW YORK

MRS. NATHAN J. MILLER, NEW ROCHELLE, NEW YORK

MR. J. B. NEUMANN, NEW YORK

MR. AND MRS. JULIUS OPPENHEIMER, NEW YORK

MR. JAMES PRESTON, NEW YORK

MRS. FANNIE M. POLLAK, NEW YORK

MR. FRANK K. M. REHN, NEW YORK

THE REINHARDT GALLERIES, NEW YORK

MRS. JOHN D. ROCKEFELLER, JR., NEW YORK

MR. AND MRS. EDWARD W. ROOT, CLINTON, NEW YORK

MR. ALBERT ROTHBART, NEW YORK

DR. B. D. SAKLATWALLA, CRAFTON, PENNSYLVANIA

MR. CHARLES F. SAMSON, NEW YORK

MR. AND MRS. LESLEY GREEN SHEAFER, NEW YORK

MR. ALFRED STIEGLITZ, NEW YORK

MR. AND MRS. REX STOUT, NEW YORK

MRS. SAMUEL TUCKER, NEW YORK

DR. W. R. VALENTINER, DETROIT

MRS. NAN WATSON, NEW YORK

MRS. HARRY PAYNE WHITNEY, NEW YORK

THE ART INSTITUTE OF CHICAGO

THE CLEVELAND MUSEUM OF ART

THE DETROIT INSTITUTE OF ART

THE FOGG ART MUSEUM, CAMBRIDGE

THE PHILLIPS MEMORIAL GALLERY, WASHINGTON

In addition to those who have lent pictures the Trustees and the Staff wish to thank for their generous co-operation in assembling the exhibition: Mr. Charles Daniel, Mrs. Edith Gregor Halpert, Mr. Alanson Hartpence, Mr. John F. Kraushaar, Mr. F. Newlin Price, Mr. Frank K. M. Rehn, Mr. and Mrs. Paul Reinhardt, Mr. Alfred Stieglitz.

FOREWORD

In its second exhibition the Museum of Modern Art presents paintings by nineteen living Americans who it is believed are fairly representative of the principal tendencies in contemporary American painting. No particular school or manner is intentionally favored. Included are artists who are so "conservative" that they are out of fashion and so "advanced" that they are not yet generally accepted. The selection is deliberately eclectic.

It seemed best to include less than twenty painters in order that a half dozen paintings by each might be shown rather than two paintings each by fifty painters or one each by a hundred. The nineteen were chosen in the following manner. Ballots containing over a hundred names were distributed among the trustees who were asked to check the fifteen painters who each thought should be shown in the Museum's first exhibition of American painting. The results were tabulated and carefully studied by a committee who drew up the list of nineteen.

Possibly several other painters might have been substituted or added, had space permitted, without affecting the standard of the exhibition. The committee wishes to emphasize the fact that future exhibitions will include many painters omitted at present.

It is interesting to observe that of the nineteen Americans five were born abroad: Karfiol, Kuniyoshi, Pascin, Sterne and Weber. A similar proportion of foreign-born artists might be found in Paris or in Germany. Three of the nineteen, Pascin, Feininger and Sterne, have lived most of their mature lives abroad, yet the United States can well afford to accept these three of her citizens who are more honored in Europe than any other American painters. America has not hesitated in the past to claim such expatriates as Whistler or Sargent or Mary Cassatt. Some of the other painters in the exhibition are perhaps more obviously and essentially American than Sterne or Weber or Pascin but it is questionable whether any are better painters. Those who chose the exhibition were concerned principally with the quality of these men as artists.

With some exceptions the paintings were selected with the advice and co-operation of the painters. In most cases it was impracticable to hang together all the paintings by one man but whenever possible several paintings by each painter have been hung so that they might be seen at the same time.

A. H. B. Jr.

CATALOG

2

BURCHFIELD · *Railroad Gantry*

17½ x 24 inches

Collection Stephen C. Clark, New York

CHARLES E. BURCHFIELD

Born at Ashtabula, Ohio, 1893
Studied at the Cleveland School of Art. Was, until last year, a professional designer of wallpapers. Lives at Gardenville, New York

1 FREIGHT CARS, *watercolor,* 1919
Private Collection, New York

2 RAILROAD GANTRY, *watercolor,* 1920
Collection Stephen C. Clark, New York

3 EATING PLACE, EAST SALEM, OHIO, *watercolor,* 1926
Collection Clifton R. Hall, Princeton, New Jersey

4 PROMENADE, *watercolor,* 1928
Private Collection, New York

5 BLACKSMITH SHOP, *watercolor,* 1928
Collection Mr. and Mrs. Edward W. Root, Clinton, New York

6 SULPHUROUS EVENING, *watercolor,* 1929
Collection Frank K. M. Rehn, New York

Other watercolors are in the following collections:

Brooklyn, Museum of Art
Buffalo, Albright Art Gallery
Cleveland, Museum of Art
New York, Metropolitan Museum of Art
Philadelphia, Pennsylvania Academy of the Fine Arts

3
BURCHFIELD · *Eating Place, East Salem, Ohio*
$14\frac{1}{4}$ x 17 inches
Collection Clifton R. Hall, Princeton, N. J.

IO

DEMUTH · *Still Life*

12 x 18 inches

Collection Ferdinand Howald, Columbus

CHARLES DEMUTH

Born in Lancaster, Pennsylvania, 1883
Studied at the Pennsylvania Academy of Fine Arts under Anschutz and others and in Paris. Lives in Lancaster

7 CIRCUS RIDER, *watercolor,* 1916
Collection Nan Watson, New York

8 DANCING SAILORS, *watercolor,* 1917
Collection Albert Rothbart, New York

9 FLOWERS, *watercolor, about* 1918
Collection Mrs. Harry Payne Whitney, New York

10 STILL LIFE, *watercolor,* 1921
Collection Ferdinand Howald, Columbus, Ohio

11 MODERN CONVENIENCES, 1922
Collection Ferdinand Howald, Columbus, Ohio

12 PAQUEBOT, PARIS, 1922
Collection Ferdinand Howald, Columbus, Ohio

13 MY EGYPT, 1927
Collection of the Artist, Lancaster, Pennsylvania

Other paintings are in the following collections:

Brooklyn, Museum of Art
Cambridge, Massachusetts, Fogg Art Museum
Chicago, Art Institute
Cleveland, Museum of Art
Columbus, Art Museum
Hartford, Connecticut, Wadsworth Atheneum
Merion, Pennsylvania, Barnes Foundation
New York, Metropolitan Museum of Art
Washington, Phillips Memorial Gallery

13
DEMUTH · *My Egypt*
36 x 30 inches
Collection of the Artist

14

DICKINSON · *Landscape with Bridge*

30½ x 24 inches

Collection Charles Daniel, New York

PRESTON DICKINSON

Born in New York, 1891

Studied at the Art Students League, New York. Lives in New York

14 LANDSCAPE WITH BRIDGE, 1922
Collection Charles Daniel, New York

15 STILL LIFE, 1924
Cleveland Museum of Art, Hinman B. Hurlbut Collection

16 OLD QUARTER, QUEBEC, 1927
Collection Phillips Memorial Gallery, Washington

17 STILL LIFE, 1928
Collection Ferdinand Howald, Columbus, Ohio

18 STILL LIFE, *pastel,* 1928
Collection Charles Daniel, New York

Other paintings are in the following collections:

Brooklyn, Museum of Art

Buffalo, Albright Art Gallery

Cambridge, Massachusetts, Fogg Art Museum

Cleveland, Museum of Art

Columbus, Art Museum

Detroit, Institute of Arts

Dublin, Ireland, National Gallery

Hartford, Connecticut, Wadsworth Atheneum

Omaha, Art Museum

Philadelphia, Pennsylvania Academy of Fine Arts

Washington, Phillips Memorial Gallery

17

DICKINSON · *Still Life*

15 x 21½ inches

Collection Ferdinand Howald, Columbus

20

FEININGER · *Sidewheeler*

31 x 39½ inches

Collection Detroit Institute of Arts

LYONEL FEININGER

Born in New York, 1870

To Hamburg 1886. Worked as caricaturist and comic strip artist for Chicago Tribune and German and French papers. First paintings, 1907, influenced by impressionism, van Gogh, and, later, cubism. Exhibited Salon des Indépendents, 1911. Exhibited with Marc, Kandinsky, and Paul Klee in first Autumn Salon, Berlin 1913. Is now professor of painting at the Bauhaus Academy at Dessau. Has recently been offered a studio by the town of Halle

19 NIEDERGRONSTADT, *ink and watercolor,* 1912
Collection J. B. Neumann, New York

20 SIDEWHEELER, 1913
Collection Detroit Institute of Art

21 IN THE VILLAGE, *ink and watercolor,* 1915
Collection J. B. Neumann, New York

22 FISHING SMACK, *ink and watercolor,* 1922
Collection Dr. W. R. Valentiner, Detroit

23 EICHELBORN, 1922
Collection Dr. W. R. Valentiner, Detroit

24 GATE TOWER I, *ink and watercolor,* 1923
Collection Mrs. Fannie M. Pollak, New York

25 SUMMER CLOUDS, *ink and watercolor,* 1927
Private Collection, New York

Other paintings are in the following collections:

Berlin, National Gallery

Cologne, Walraff-Richartz Museum

(Continued on following page)

Detroit, Institute of Arts
Dresden, Gallery
Dusseldorf, Gallery
Erfurt, Gallery
Essen, Civic Museum
Frankfort-on-Main, Staedel Institute
Halle, Art Gallery
Hamburg, Art Gallery
Mannheim, Art Gallery
Moscow, Museum of Modern Western Art
Oslo, National Gallery
Stockholm, National Museum
Weimar, Gallery

Etchings and woodcuts by Feininger are in other museums.

24

FEININGER · *Gate Tower I*

$13\frac{1}{4}$ x 10 inches

Collection Mrs. Fannie M. Pollak, New York

26

HART · *Mule Car, Mexico*

18 x 25 inches

Collection Dr. B. D. Saklatwalla, Crafton, Pa.

GEORGE OVERBURY "POP" HART

Born in Cairo, Illinois, 1868

Received little formal instruction. Travelled and painted in Italy, Egypt, Tahiti, Samoa, Hawaii, Iceland, West Indies, Paris, Mexico, and Morocco. Supported himself until recently by painting signs and movie sets. He lives (occasionally) at Coytesville, New Jersey

26 MULE CAR, MEXICO, 1926
Collection Dr. B. D. Saklatwalla, Crafton, Pennsylvania

27 FRUIT GATHERERS, TEUNTEPEC, MEXICO, 1927
Private Collection, New York

28 THE JURY, MEXICO, 1928
Private Collection, New York

29 THE MERRY-GO-ROUND, OAXACA, MEXICO, 1927
Private Collection, New York

30 LANDSCAPE, MOROCCO, 1929
Collection Downtown Gallery, New York

Other paintings are in the following collections:

Brooklyn, Museum of Art
Chicago, Art Institute
Cincinnati, Art Museum
Cleveland, Museum of Art
London, South Kensington Museum
Los Angeles, Museum of History, Science and Art
Mexico City, National Museum
Newark, Art Museum
New York, Metropolitan Museum of Art

Etchings and lithographs by Hart are in other museums.

9

ART · *Merry-Go-Round, Oaxaca, Mexico*

x 23 inches

vate Collection, New York

31
HOPPER · *House by the Railroad*
24 x 29½ inches
Collection Stephen C. Clark, New York

EDWARD HOPPER

Born in Nyack, New York, 1882
Studied in New York under Chase, Kenneth Hayes Miller, and Robert Henri
Lives in New York

31 HOUSE BY THE RAILROAD, 1925
Collection Stephen C. Clark, New York

32 HOUSE OF THE FOG HORN, *watercolor*, 1927
Collection Mrs. John O. Blanchard, New York

33 AUTOMAT, 1927
Collection Mr. and Mrs.Lesley Green Sheafer, New York

34 BLACKWELLS ISLAND, 1928
Collection William Russell Allen, Boston

35 FREIGHT CARS AT GLOUCESTER, 1928
Collection Mr. and Mrs. Edward W. Root, Clinton, New York

36 LIGHTHOUSE, 1929
Collection Mrs. Samuel Tucker, New York

Other paintings are in the following collections:

Brooklyn, Museum
Cambridge, Massachusetts, Fogg Art Museum
Chicago, Art Institute
Hartford, Connecticut, Wadsworth Atheneum
New Orleans, Delgado Museum of Art
New York, Metropolitan Museum of Art
Philadelphia, Pennsylvania Academy of Fine Arts
Washington, Phillips Memorial Gallery

Etchings by Hopper are in other museums.

35

HOPPER · *Freight Cars at Gloucester*

29 x 40 inches

Collection Mr. and Mrs. Edward W. Root, Clinton, N. Y.

39
KARFIOL · *Three Seated Figures*
30 x 41 inches
Collection Downtown Gallery, New York

BERNARD KARFIOL

Born near Budapesth of American parents, 1886
Studied without a master in New York and Paris
Lives in New York

37 BOY, 1922
Collection Phillips Memorial Gallery, Washington

38 CROSSROADS, 1924
Collection Dr. and Mrs. F. H. Hirschland, New York

39 THREE SEATED FIGURES, 1927
Collection Downtown Gallery, New York

40 RECLINING NUDE, 1928
Collection Downtown Gallery, New York

41 SEATED NUDE, 1929
Collection Downtown Gallery, New York

Other paintings are in the following collections:

Newark, Art Museum
Washington, Corcoran Art Gallery
Washington, Phillips Memorial Gallery

41

KARFIOL · *Seated Nude*

40 x 30 inches

Collection Downtown Gallery, New York

43

KENT · *Toilers of the Sea*

37½ x 44 inches

Collection Adolph Lewisohn, New York

ROCKWELL KENT

Born at Tarrytown Heights, New York, 1882
Studied under William Chase, Robert Henri, Kenneth Hayes Miller, and Abbott Thayer. Has traveled and painted in Alaska, Tierra del Fuego, Iceland and Greenland. Lives in Ausable Forks, New York

42 LANDSCAPE, VERMONT, 1909
Private Collection, New York

43 TOILERS OF THE SEA, 1907
Collection Adolph Lewisohn, New York

44 BURIAL OF A YOUNG MAN
Collection Phillips Memorial Gallery, Washington

45 VOYAGING, 1923
Collection Phillips Memorial Gallery, Washington

46 CROMLECH, 1925
Collection Mr. and Mrs. Rex Stout, New York

Other paintings are in the following collections:

Brooklyn, Museum of Art
Chicago, Art Institute
New York, Metropolitan Museum of Art

Woodcuts by Kent are in other museums.

45
KENT · *Voyaging*
28 x 56 inches
Collection Phillips Memorial Gallery, Washington

49

KUHN · *Jeannette*

30 x 25¼ inches

Private Collection, New York

WALT KUHN

Born in New York, 1880
Studied painting in Paris, Munich, Holland and Italy
Lives in New York

47 BAREBACK RIDER, 1926
Collection Downtown Gallery, New York

48 ATHENE, 1927
Private Collection, New York

49 JEANNETTE, 1928
Private Collection, New York

50 THE WHITE CLOWN, 1929
Private Collection, New York

51 ELECTRA, 1929
Private Collection, New York

Other paintings are in the following collections:

Brooklyn, Art Museum
Chicago, Art Institute
Los Angeles, Museum, Preston Harrison Collection
Washington, Phillips Memorial Gallery

50
KUHN · *The White Clown*
40 x 30½ inches
Private Collection, New York

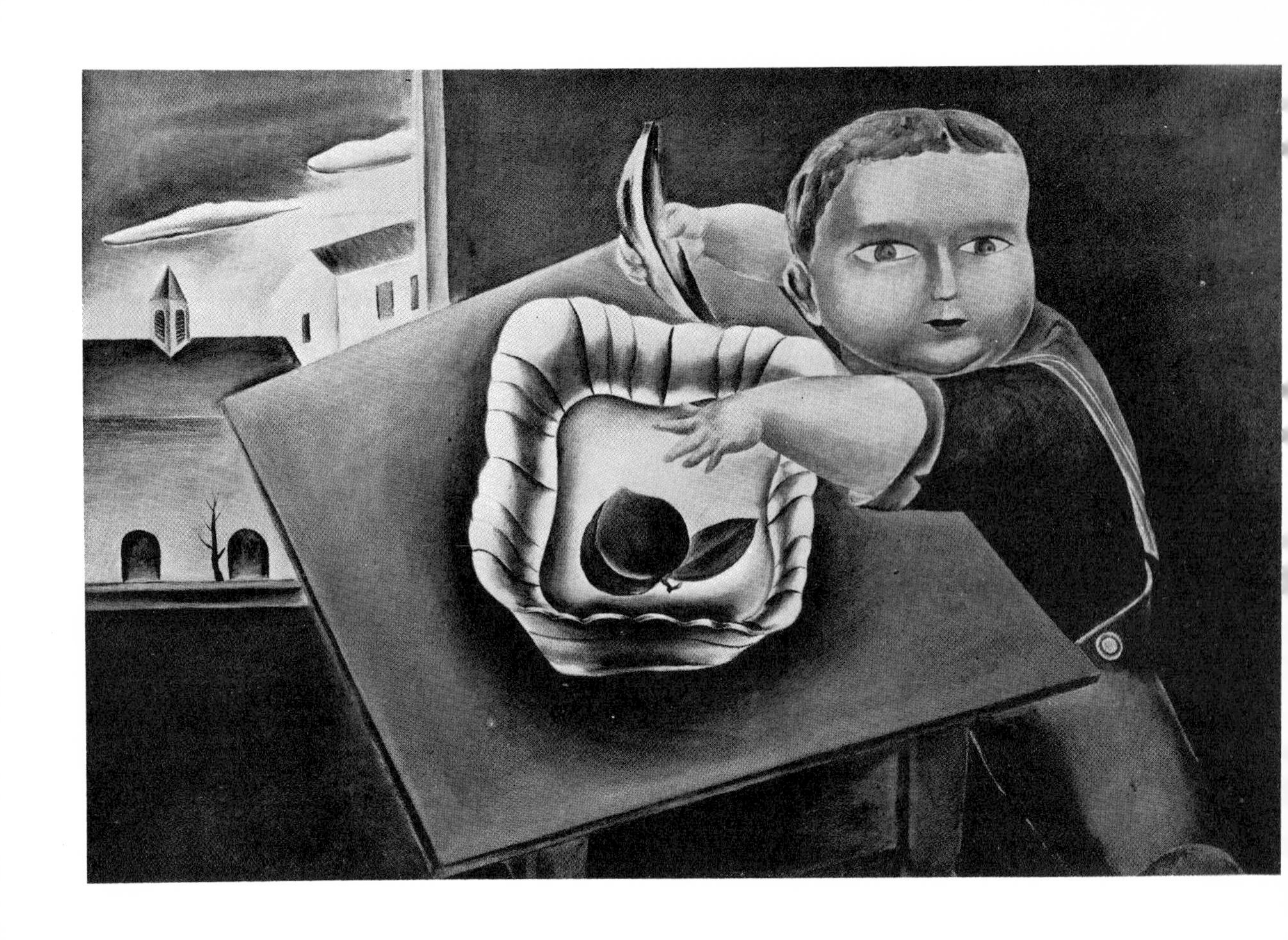

52

KUNIYOSHI · *Boy Stealing Fruit*

19½ x 29½ inches

Collection Ferdinand Howald, Columbus

YASUO KUNIYOSHI

Born at Okayama, Japan, 1893
Studied in Los Angeles and later in New York under Kenneth Hayes Miller. Works as a professional photographer. Lives in Brooklyn

52 BOY STEALING FRUIT, 1923
Collection Ferdinand Howald, Columbus, Ohio

53 LANDSCAPE, MAINE, 1925
Collection Ferdinand Howald, Columbus, Ohio

54 SELF PORTRAIT AS GOLF PLAYER, 1927
Collection Charles Daniel, New York

55 NUDE, 1929
Collection Charles Daniel, New York

56 STILL LIFE, 1929
Collection Charles Daniel, New York

Other paintings are in the collection of

New York University, Gallery of Living Art

54

KUNIYOSHI · *Self Portrait as Golf Player*

50 x 40 inches

Collection Charles Daniel, New York

60

LAWSON · *After Rain*

24 x 30 inches

Collection Phillips Memorial Gallery, Washington

ERNEST LAWSON

Born in San Francisco, 1873
Studied in Kansas City, Paris, and at the Art Students League, New York. Influenced by Twachtman

57 RIVER BANK
Collection James Preston, New York

58 THE WHITE HORSE
Collection James Preston, New York

59 SPRING NIGHT, HARLEM RIVER, 1913
Collection Phillips Memorial Gallery, Washington

60 AFTER RAIN, 1915
Collection Phillips Memorial Gallery, Washington

61 HARLEM RIVER, WINTER, 1915
Collection A. E. Gallatin, New York

Other paintings are in the following collections:

Brooklyn, Museum of Art
Chicago, Art Institute
Merion, Pennsylvania, Barnes Foundation
Montclair, New Jersey, Art Museum
New York, Metropolitan Museum of Art
Pittsburgh, Carnegie Institute
Saint Louis, City Art Museum
Savannah, Georgia, Telfair Academy of Art
Washington, Corcoran Art Gallery
Washington, Phillips Memorial Gallery
Worcester, Art Museum

1

AWSON · *Harlem River, Winter*

5 x 20½ inches

ollection A. E. Gallatin, New York

62

MARIN · *Maine Islands*

16½ x 19½ inches

Collection Phillips Memorial Gallery, Washington

JOHN MARIN

Born at Rutherford, New Jersey, 1870
Studied at the Pennsylvania Academy of Fine Arts, the New York Art Students League, and in Paris

62 MAINE ISLANDS, 1922
Collection Phillips Memorial Gallery, Washington

63 RED LIGHTNING, 1922
Collection Ferdinand Howald, Columbus, Ohio

64 BACK OF BEAR MOUNTAIN, 1925
Collection Phillips Memorial Gallery, Washington

65 SAIL BOAT, 1926
Collection Mrs. Charles Liebman, New York

66 PRESIDENTIAL RANGE, 1927
Collection Fogg Art Museum, Cambridge

67 FRANCONIA NOTCH AND ECHO LAKE, 1927
Collection Alfred Stieglitz, New York

Other water colors are in the following collections:

Brooklyn, Museum of Art
Cambridge, Massachusetts, Fogg Art Museum
Chicago, Art Institute
New York, Metropolitan Museum of Art
Washington, Phillips Memorial Gallery

Etchings by Marin are in other museums.

64

MARIN · *Back of Bear Mountain*

17½ x 20½ inches

Collection Phillips Memorial Gallery, Washington

69

MILLER · *Shoppers in the Rain*

30 x 25½ inches

Collection Mrs. G. Warrington Curtis, New York

KENNETH HAYES MILLER

Born at Oneida, New York, 1876

Studied at The Art Students League and the New York School of Art. In Europe 1900. Was a pupil of Mowbray, Cox, and Chase; influenced by Albert P. Ryder. Instructor in drawing and painting at the New York School of Art 1899-1911; the Art Students League since 1911. Lives in New York

68 PORTRAIT OF ALBERT P. RYDER, 1913
Collection Phillips Memorial Gallery, Washington

69 SHOPPERS IN THE RAIN, 1928
Collection Mrs. G. Warrington Curtis, New York

70 PREPARATIONS, 1928
Collection Frank K. M. Rehn, New York

71 SHOPPER, 1928
Collection Frank K. M. Rehn, New York

72 MOTHER AND CHILD WITH TOY BALLOON, 1929
Collection Frank K. M. Rehn, New York

Other paintings are in the following collections:

Cleveland, Museum of Art

Los Angeles, Museum, Preston Harrison Collection

New York, Metropolitan Museum of Art

Washington, Phillips Memorial Gallery

Etchings by Miller are in other museums.

70

MILLER · *Preparations*

30 x 24 inches

Collection Frank K. M. Rehn, New York

73
O'KEEFFE · *Grey Tree*
36 x 30 inches
Collection of the Artist, New York

GEORGIA O'KEEFFE

Born at Sun Prairie, Wisconsin, 1887

Studied at the Chicago Art Institute under Vanderpoel and in New York at the Art Students League under Chase; later at the Teachers College under Bement and Dow. Taught school in Texas and later returned to New York where she now lives

73 GREY TREE, 1925
Collection of the Artist, New York

74 RADIATOR BUILDING, 1927
Collection of the Artist, New York

75 WHITE PANSY, 1927
Collection of the Artist, New York

76 PINK SWEET PEAS, *pastel,* 1927
Collection of the Artist, New York

77 WHITE CALLA LILIES, 1928
Collection of the Artist, New York

Other paintings are in the following collections:

Brooklyn, Museum of Art

Washington, Phillips Memorial Gallery

74

O'KEEFFE · *Radiator Building*

48 x 30 inches

Collection of the Artist, New York

78

PASCIN · *Susannah and the Elders*

31½ x 24 inches

Private Collection, New York

JULES PASCIN

Born at Widden, Bulgaria, 1885
Studied in art schools in Vienna. Worked for a time in Germany where he had his first success. Paris in 1905; afterwards, Egypt, Spain, Tunis. During the war he was in America working in New York, Charleston, New Orleans, and Havana. Became an American citizen but at present lives in Paris

78 SUSANNAH AND THE ELDERS
Private Collection, New York

79 PORTRAIT OF HERMINE DAVID
Private Collection, New York

80 CAFE, NEW ORLEANS
Collection Ferdinand Howald, Columbus, Ohio

81 SEATED GIRL, 1927
Private Collection, New York

82 MARY, 1928
Collection Downtown Gallery, New York

Other paintings are in the following collections:

Bremen, Art Gallery
Cologne, Walraff-Richartz Museum
Dresden, Picture Gallery
Hamburg, Art Gallery
Merion, Pennsylvania, Barnes Foundation

80

PASCIN · *Café, New Orleans*

8 x 12 inches

Collection Ferdinand Howald, Columbus

83

SLOAN · *Wake of Ferry Boat*

28 x 34 inches

Collection Phillips Memorial Gallery, Washington

JOHN SLOAN

Born at Lock Haven, Pennsylvania, 1871
Studied at the night school of the Pennsylvania Academy of Fine Arts under Anschutz. Instructor, Art Students League since 1914 and Director of the Society of Independent Artists. Lives in New York

83 WAKE OF FERRYBOAT, 1907
Collection Phillips Memorial Gallery, Washington

84 OLD CLOWN, 1910
Collection Phillips Memorial Gallery, Washington

85 RENGANESCHI'S, 1912
Collection of Art Institute of Chicago

86 BACKYARD, GREENWICH VILLAGE, 1914
Collection of the Artist, New York

87 GOING TO CHURCH, NEW MEXICO, 1925
Collection Albert Rothbart, New York

Other paintings are in the following collections:

Brooklyn, Museum of Art
Chicago, Art Institute
Cincinnati, Art Museum
Detroit, Institute of Arts
Los Angeles, Art Museum
Merion, Pennsylvania, Barnes Foundation
Newark, Art Museum
New York, Metropolitan Museum of Art
State College, Pennsylvania, Museum

(Continued on following page)

Pittsburgh, Carnegie Institute
Sante Fe, New Mexico Gallery of Art
Washington, Phillips Memorial Gallery

Etchings by Sloan are in other museums.

86

SLOAN · *Backyard, Greenwich Village*

26 x 32 inches

Collection of the Artist, New York

88

SPEICHER · *Torso of Hilda*

34 x 31½ inches

Collection Detroit Institute of Arts

EUGENE SPEICHER

Born in Buffalo, 1883
Studied at the Albright Art School, Buffalo, The Art Students League and the Henri Art School in New York and in Europe.
Lives in New York

88 TORSO OF HILDA, 1927
Collection Detroit Institute of Art

89 BRIGHAMS YARD, EAST KINGSTON, 1927
Collection Mr. and Mrs. Edward W. Root, Clinton, New York

90 OLD BOATS, RONDOUT, 1927
Collection Charles F. Samson, New York

91 FLOWERS, 1927
Private Collection, New York

92 MOUNTAINEER, 1929
Collection Stephen C. Clark, New York

Other paintings are in the following collections:

Buffalo, Albright Art Gallery
Cambridge, Massachusetts, Fogg Art Museum
Cleveland, Museum of Art
Decater, Illinois, Institute of Arts
Des Moines, Art Museum
Detroit, Institute of Arts
Galveston, Art Museum
Minneapolis, Art Museum
New York, Metropolitan Museum of Art
Washington, Phillips Memorial Gallery

91
SPEICHER · *Flowers*
25¼ x 22 inches
Private Collection, New York

97
STERNE · *Girl with Blackberries*
37 x 46 inches
Collection Detroit Institute of Arts

MAURICE STERNE

Born at Libau, Latvia, 1877
Came to New York at an early age. Studied at the National Academy of Design. To Paris in 1904; then to Italy and Greece. Settled at Anticoli in Italy, but lived for several years, 1911-14, on the island of Bali, Dutch East Indies. Has divided his recent years between Anticoli and New York

93 BALI CHILD, 1911-14
Collection Miss Dorothy Borg, New York

94 EGGS AND WATER PITCHER, 1923
Private Collection, New York

95 GIRL IN BLUE CHAIR, 1928
Collection Mr. and Mrs. Samuel A. Lewisohn, New York

96 HEAD OF A GIRL, 1928
Private Collection, New York

97 GIRL WITH BLACKBERRIES, 1928
Collection Detroit Institute of Arts

98 GREEN PEARS, 1929
Collection Reinhardt Galleries, New York

Other paintings are in the following collections:

Detroit, Institute of Arts
Florence, Pitti Gallery (Self Portrait)
Pittsburgh, Carnegie Institute
Providence, Rhode Island School of Design
Washington, Phillips Memorial Collection

Sculpture and Drawings by Sterne are in other museums.

98

STERNE · *Green Pears*

20 x 26½ inches

Collection Reinhardt Galleries, New York

102

WEBER · *Alone*

36 x 30 inches

Collection Downtown Gallery, New York

MAX WEBER

Born at Vialostok, U.S.S.R. in 1881
Studied with Dow in New York and Laurens and Matisse in Paris, 1905-1908. Instructor New York Art Students League, 1920-26
Lives now at Great Neck, Long Island

99 THE WORSHIPPER, 1918
Collection Mrs. Nathan J. Miller, New Rochelle, New York

100 DEATH BED, *gouache*, 1918
Collection Mr. and Mrs. Julius Oppenheimer

101 TWO FIGURES, *gouache*, 1918
Collection Mr. and Mrs. Julius Oppenheimer

102 ALONE, 1927
Collection Downtown Gallery, New York

103 LANDSCAPE, 1927
Collection Mrs. Edward A. Jordan, New York

104 STILL LIFE WITH A LOAF OF BREAD, 1929
Private Collection, New York

105 STILL LIFE WITH THREE JUGS, 1929
Collection Downtown Gallery, New York

Other paintings are in the following collections:

Los Angeles, Art Museum
New York University, Gallery of Living Art
Washington, Phillips Memorial Gallery

Woodcuts by Weber are in other museums.

104
WEBER · *Still Life with a Loaf of Bread*
20 x 24½ inches
Private Collection, New York

This catalog was issued in January 1930, by the Trustees of The Museum of Modern Art, in New York. First edition, 2250 copies.

PAINTING AND SCULPTURE BY LIVING AMERICANS

NINTH LOAN EXHIBITION

DECEMBER 2, 1930 TO JANUARY 20, 1931

MUSEUM OF MODERN ART

NEW YORK

ACKNOWLEDGMENTS

The exhibition has been selected from the following collections

AN AMERICAN PLACE, NEW YORK
EDWARD DUFF BALKEN, PITTSBURGH
JAY H. BARNUM, NORWALK, CONNECTICUT
MISS L. P. BLISS, NEW YORK
MRS. W. MURRAY CRANE, NEW YORK
FRANK CROWNINSHIELD, NEW YORK
THE CHESTER DALE COLLECTION, NEW YORK
THE DANIEL GALLERY, NEW YORK
THE DOWNTOWN GALLERY, NEW YORK
MRS. MURIEL DRAPER, NEW YORK
JOHN A. DUNBAR, NEW YORK
MRS. JULIANA R. FORCE, NEW YORK
A. CONGER GOODYEAR, NEW YORK
EDWARD S. GREENBAUM, NEW YORK
DR. F. H. HIRSCHLAND, NEW YORK
EARL HORTER, PHILADELPHIA
JOEL T. HOWARD, DALLAS, TEXAS
SIDNEY JANOWITZ, NEW YORK
KRAUSHAAR GALLERIES, NEW YORK
MR. AND MRS. SAMUEL A. LEWISOHN, NEW YORK
MRS. CHARLES J. LIEBMAN, NEW YORK
THE MACBETH GALLERIES, NEW YORK
MRS. MALCOLM L. McBRIDE, CLEVELAND, OHIO
GLENN FORD McKINNEY, NEW YORK
DR. AND MRS. JAMES B. MURPHY, NEW YORK
GUSTAVE NASSAUER, NEW YORK
J. B. NEUMANN, NEW YORK
MISS MARJORIE PATTERSON, NEW YORK
MURDOCK PEMBERTON, NEW YORK
THE PHILLIPS MEMORIAL GALLERY, WASHINGTON
GEORGE D. PRATT, JR., BRIDGEWATER, CONNECTICUT
RALPH PULITZER, NEW YORK
THE FRANK K. M. REHN GALLERY, NEW YORK
MRS. JOHN D. ROCKEFELLER, JR., NEW YORK

EDWARD W. ROOT, CLINTON, NEW YORK
PAUL ROSENFELD, NEW YORK
EUGENE SCHOEN, INC., NEW YORK
JACQUES SELIGMANN & COMPANY, NEW YORK AND PARIS
MRS. ELEANOR C. SHEPARDSON, NEW YORK
MRS. M. DESILVER, BROOKLYN
HERBERT A. SPEISER, PHILADELPHIA
MAURICE J. SPEISER, PHILADELPHIA
ALFRED STIEGLITZ, NEW YORK
HARRY SUNDHEIM, PHILADELPHIA
WEYHE GALLERY, NEW YORK
DR. NATHAN WOLF, NEW YORK
THE ALBRIGHT ART GALLERY, BUFFALO
THE MUSEUM OF THE BROOKLYN INSTITUTE OF ARTS AND SCIENCES, BROOKLYN

In addition to those who have lent pictures the Trustees and the Staff of the Museum wish to thank for their generous co-operation in assembling the exhibition:

Mr. Edward Duff Balken, Mrs. Mary T. Bullard, Mr. John Clancy, Mr. John O'Connor, Jr., Mr. Charles Daniel, Mrs. Muriel Draper, Mrs. Edith Gregor Halpert, Mr. William M. Hekking, Mr. E. C. Holston, Mr. Samuel M. Kootz, Miss A. M. Kraushaar, Mr. Julien Levy, Mr. Robert W. Macbeth, Mr. Robert C. McIntyre, Mr. J. B. Neumann, Miss M. L. Nourse, Mr. Frank K. M. Rehn, Mr. Maurice Speiser, Mr. Alfred Stieglitz, Mr. James St. L. O'Toole, Mr. Herbert B. Tschudy, Dr. Carl Zigrosser.

TRUSTEES

FOREWORD

In its Ninth Loan Exhibition the Museum of Modern Art presents the work of thirty American painters and seven sculptors none of whose work has previously been exhibited either in the Museum's Second Exhibition, "Paintings by Nineteen Living Americans," or in its Fifth Exhibition, "46 Painters and Sculptors under 35".

While in a sense supplementary to these two earlier exhibitions it is believed that the present exhibition may even exceed them in interest because it includes not only many of the best-known American painters and sculptors but also several who have hitherto been practically unrecognized in New York.

The Exhibition was selected by a Committee formed by four of the Trustees in conjunction with the two directors. The Museum's policy of choosing artists regardless of school is continued. As a result painters are included who are followers of the Impressionists as well as others who paint in more recent manners.

American sculpture except by younger artists has up till now been somewhat neglected by the Museum. The present Exhibition will therefore be of especial importance to those interested in the work of American sculptors.

It was originally intended to include work by Thomas Benton and Maurice Sterne. Mr. Benton, however, is devoting himself to mural painting and prefers not to exhibit his canvases while Mr. Sterne's recent sculpture is in Italy and could not be secured in time for the present exhibition. It is hoped that their work will be exhibited in the future.

A. H. B., JR.

CATALOG

PAINTINGS

An asterisk before a number indicates that the work is illustrated by a plate bearing the same number.

GIFFORD BEAL

Born in New York in 1879. Pupil of Chase at Shinnecock and of Ranger at the Art Students' League. Lives in New York City

*1 FISHERMAN'S DAUGHTER, 1930
Collection Kraushaar Galleries, New York

2 THE POLKA FROM *DIE FLEDERMAUS*, 1930
Collection Kraushaar Galleries, New York

3 ROCKPORT QUARRY, 1930
Collection Kraushaar Galleries, New York

PAUL BURLIN

Born in New York in 1886. Studied in England and Paris. Spent much time in the South West of the United States. Has lived since 1921 in Paris

4 FLOWERS, 1927
Collection Dr. F. H. Hirschland, New York

*5 HORSES IN STABLE, *about* 1928
Collection Mrs. M. deSilver, New York

6 HILLS AND HOUSES
Collection Jacques Seligmann and Company, New York and Paris

VINCENT CANADÉ

Born in Alvenese, Italy, in 1879. Largely self taught. Lives in New York

7 DOUBLE SELF-PORTRAIT, *about* 1919
Private Collection E. Weyhe, New York

*8 THE ARTIST'S FAMILY, *about* 1924
Collection Weyhe Gallery, New York

9 ROOF TOPS, 1927
Collection Weyhe Gallery, New York

ARTHUR CARLES

Born in Philadelphia in 1882. Studied at Pennsylvania Academy of Fine Arts. Lives in Philadelphia

10 LANDSCAPE, 1912
Collection Maurice J. Speiser, Philadelphia

11 NUDE, 1922
Collection Herbert A. Speiser, Philadelphia

*12 CALLA LILIES, 1927
Collection Harry Sundheim, Philadelphia

JAMES CHAPIN

Born in West Orange, New Jersey, in 1887. Studied at Cooper Union and Art Students' League. Lives in New Jersey

13 ALINE McMAHON
Private Collection Frank K. M. Rehn, New York

14 THE PRETZEL MAN, 1929
Collection the Artist

*15 BOXER AND HIS MANAGER, 1930
Collection Frank K. M. Rehn Gallery, New York

MERTON CLIVETTE

Born on the S.S. Enterprise in the Indian Ocean in 1848. Studied at the Art Students' League. Formerly professional acrobat, magician, and publicity agent. Lives in New York

*16 JUNGLE ARGUMENT
Collection Gustave Nassauer, New York

17 THE BARONESS
Collection Gustave Nassauer, New York

18 SEATTLE SQUAW
Collection Gustave Nassauer, New York

ANDREW DASBURG

Born of American Parents in Paris in 1887. Pupil of Cox, Harrison and Henri in New York. Lives in Santa Fe, New Mexico

19 LANDSCAPE, LAMY, NEW MEXICO, 1927
Collection Frank K. M. Rehn Gallery, New York

*20 POPPIES
Collection Mr. and Mrs. Jay H. Barnum, Norwalk, Connecticut

21 MERGANSER, 1930
Private Collection, New York

STUART DAVIS

Born in Philadelphia in 1894. Studied with Henri. Lived for a time in Paris but now lives in New York

22 TABLE, *about* 1925
Collection Downtown Gallery New York

23 PLACE DES VOSGES, 1929
Private Collection, New York

*24 SUMMER LANDSCAPE, 1930
Collection Downtown Gallery, New York

PAUL DOUGHERTY

Born in Brooklyn in 1877. Studied alone, Paris, London, Florence, Venice, and Munich. Lives at present in California

25 FLOWERS, *about* 1925
Private Collection, New York

26 CAÑON AFTER RAIN, 1930
Collection the Artist

*27 SHADOWED MESA, 1930
Collection the Artist

ARTHUR G. DOVE

Born in Canandaigua, New York, in 1880. Worked at first as an illustrator. Lives at Halesite, Long Island

*28 DISTRACTION, 1929
Collection An American Place, New York

29 COLORED BARGEMAN, 1929
Collection An American Place, New York

30 HARBOR IN LIGHT, 1929
Collection An American Place, New York

GUY PENE DUBOIS

Born in Brooklyn in 1884. Pupil of Chase, DuMond, and Henri. Has lived in Paris recently; at present in New York

31 RESTAURANT (1), 1924
The Chester Dale Collection, New York

32 RESTAURANT (2), 1924
The Chester Dale Collection, New York

*33 CAFÉ BREAKFAST, 1929
Collection Kraushaar Galleries, New York

ERNEST FIENE

Born in the Rhineland, Germany, in 1894. Studied at the National Academy of Design. Lives in Woodstock, N. Y.

34 HUDSON RIVER BOAT, 1929
Collection Frank K. M. Rehn Gallery, New York

*35 RAZING BUILDINGS, 49TH STREET, 1930
Collection Frank K. M. Rehn Gallery, New York

36 SHOW GIRL, No. 2, 1930
Collection Frank K. M. Rehn Gallery, New York

ARNOLD FRIEDMAN

Born in New York in 1879. Studied at the Art Students' League and under Robert Henri. Lives at Corona, Long Island, N. Y.

37 FATHER X, 1927
Collection Dr. Nathan Wolf, New York

*38 WHITE PONY, 1928
Collection Mrs. Charles J. Liebman, New York

39 STILL LIFE, 1929
Collection Downtown Gallery, New York

WILLIAM GLACKENS

Born in Philadelphia in 1870. Studied at Pennsylvania Academy of Art. Lives in New York

*40 DREAM RIDE, 1923
Collection Kraushaar Galleries, New York

41 FLOWERS, 1930
Collection Kraushaar Galleries, New York

MARSDEN HARTLEY

Born in Lewiston, Maine, in 1878. Studied at Cleveland School of Fine Arts and at the Chase School in New York. Studied at the National Academy of Design under Cox, Chase, DuMond, and F. Luis Mora. Has worked in Germany and France. Lives in New York

42 PORTRAIT OF MY FRIEND, 1914
Collection An American Place, New York

43 RUBBER PLANT, 1922
Collection Paul Rosenfeld, New York

*44 GRAPES, 1927
Collection Phillips Memorial Gallery, Washington

CHILDE HASSAM

Born in Boston in 1859. Studied in Paris with Boulanger and Lefèvre. Lives in New York

45 VAL DE GRACE, 1888
Collection Joel T. Howard, Dallas, Texas

*46 SPRING IN WEST 78TH STREET, 1905
Private Collection, New York

47 FLAGS ON 57TH STREET, WINTER, 1918
Collection the Artist

JOHN KANE

Born of Irish Parents in West Calder, Scotland, in 1859. Came to America in 1880. No formal art training. Earns his living as a house-painter. Lives in Pittsburgh

*48 HOMESTEAD
Collection the Artist

49 ESCAPE
Collection the Artist

50 SQUIRREL HILL FARM
Collection Edward Duff Balken, Pittsburgh

MORRIS KANTOR

Born in Russia in 1896. Came to United States when thirteen years old. Pupil of Homer Boss in New York. Lives in New York

51 ODE TO THE ANTIQUE, 1929
Collection Frank K. M. Rehn Gallery, New York

*52 OUT THE WINDOW, 1930
Collection Frank K. M. Rehn Gallery, New York

53 OFF SHORE, 1930
Collection Frank K. M. Rehn Gallery, New York

CARL KNATHS

Born in Eau Claire, Wisconsin, in 1891. Studied at the Art Institute of Chicago. Lives in Provincetown, Massachusetts

*54 COCK AND GLOVE, 1927
Collection Phillips Memorial Gallery, Washington

55 THE POND, 1930. *Watercolor*
Collection Daniel Gallery, New York

56 HOUSES, 1930. *Watercolor*
Collection Daniel Gallery, New York

BENJAMIN KOPMAN

Born in Russia in 1887. Studied under Jones, Maynard and Ward at the National Academy of Design

57 PORTRAIT
Collection Alfred Stieglitz, New York

58 HEAD, 1929
Collection Sidney Janowitz, New York

*59 LANDSCAPE, 1930
Collection J. B. Neumann, New York

LEON KROLL

Born in New York in 1884. Studied at the Art Students' League, the National Academy of Design, and under Laurens in Paris. Lives in New York

60 CENTRAL PARK, 1923
Collection Ralph Pulitzer, New York

61 SERENA, 1930
Collection Frank K. M. Rehn Gallery, New York

*62 FOLLY COVE, 1930
Collection Frank K. M. Rehn Gallery, New York

SIDNEY LAUFMAN

Born in Cleveland in 1891. Studied at the Art Institute of Chicago, 1912–1916; Art Students' League, 1916–1918; Paris 1920–1930

*63 LANDSCAPE, 1930
Collection the Artist

64 STILL LIFE, 1930
Collection the Artist

GEORGE BENJAMIN LUKS

Born in Williamsport, Pennsylvania, in 1867. Studied at Pennsylvania Academy and later in Düsseldorf, Paris, and London

65 OTIS SKINNER AS COLONEL PHILIPPE BRIDAU IN "THE HONOR OF THE FAMILY"
Collection Phillips Memorial Gallery, Washington

66 SATURDAY NIGHT, 1925
Collection Frank K. M. Rehn Gallery, New York

*67 ELEANOR, 1927
Collection Frank K. M. Rehn Gallery, New York

HENRY LEE McFEE

Born in St. Louis in 1886. Studied at the Art Students' League School in Woodstock, N. Y. Lives in Woodstock, N. Y.

68 MAN IN HIGH HAT, SELF PORTRAIT, 1925
Collection Albright Art Gallery, Buffalo

*69 LEAVES, 1927
Collection Edward W. Root, Clinton, New York

70 STILL-LIFE WITH A BLUE BOWL, 1928
Collection Frank K. M. Rehn Gallery, New York

BOARDMAN ROBINSON

Born in Somerset, Nova Scotia, in 1876. Studied at Massachusetts Normal Art School, and in Paris at the Academie Colarossi, and the École des Beaux-Arts. Lives in New York

71 "SERBIA, MY DEAR MOTHER," 1916. *Watercolor*
Illustration for John Reed's *The War in Eastern Europe*
Collection Mrs. Malcolm L. McBride, Cleveland

72 THE WOMAN OF SAMARIA, 1921
Private Collection, New York

*73 SERMON ON THE MOUNT, 1926. *Oil over tempera on plaster*
Collection Eugene Schoen, Inc., New York

HENRY SCHNAKENBERG

Born in New Brighton, New York, in 1892. Studied with Kenneth Hayes Miller. Lives in New York

*74 STILL-LIFE WITH A RED BANDANA, 1929
Collection Kraushaar Galleries, New York

75 WHEATFIELD
Collection Kraushaar Galleries, New York

CHARLES SHEELER

Born in Philadelphia in 1883. Studied at the Pennsylvania Academy of Fine Arts, and under Chase in New York. Lives in New York

76 PENNSYLVANIA BARN, 1922. *Tempera and crayon*
Collection Mrs. Juliana R. Force, New York

77 PERTAINING TO YACHTS AND YACHTING, 1923
Collection Earl Horter, Philadelphia

78 PEARS ON A PINK PLATE, 1924. *Crayon*
Collection Daniel Gallery, New York

79 UPPER DECK, 1929
Collection Downtown Gallery, New York

*80 AMERICAN LANDSCAPE, 1930
Collection the Artist

NILES SPENCER

Born in Pawtucket, Rhode Island, in 1893. Studied at Rhode Island School of Design, and in New York under Henri and Bellows. Lives in New York

81 INTERIOR, 1925
Collection Edward S. Greenbaum, New York

82 ORDNANCE DOCK, BERMUDA, 1928
Collection Mr. and Mrs. Samuel A. Lewisohn, New York

*83 WHITE FACTORY, 1929
Collection Daniel Gallery, New York

AUGUSTUS VINCENT TACK

Born in Pittsburgh in 1870. Studied with Merson in Paris, and with Mowbray and LaFarge in New York

*84 LARGO, 1928
Collection Phillips Memorial Gallery, Washington

85 FLIGHT, 1930
Collection Phillips Memorial Gallery, Washington

86 FAR REACHES, 1930
Collection Phillips Memorial Gallery, Washington

MARK TOBEY

Born in Wisconsin. Has worked in Chicago, New York, and Seattle where he now lives

*87 AMERICAN LANDSCAPE, 1928
Collection the Artist

88 PORTRAIT OF A POET, 1928
Collection the Artist

89 VICTORY, 1928
Collection the Artist

SCULPTORS

Note: In order to facilitate the arrangement of the sculpture more has been borrowed than can actually be shown.

ALEXANDER CALDER

Born in Philadelphia in 1899. Studied at the Art Students' League, New York. Lives in Paris

*90 COW. *Wood*
Collection George D. Pratt, Jr., Bridgewater, Connecticut

91 STOOPING GIRL. *Wood*
Collection the Artist, New York

92 MAN. *Wood*
Collection J. B. Neumann, New York

93 ACROBATS. *Wood*
Collection J. B. Neumann, New York

HUNT DIEDERICH

Born in Nuremberg in 1884. Studied in Europe. Lives in New York

*94 WRESTLERS. *Stone*
Collection Downtown Gallery, New York

95 SPANISH HORSEMAN. *Bronze*
Collection Dr. and Mrs. James B. Murphy, New York

ANNA GLENNY

Born in Buffalo in 1888. Studied with Bela Pratt at the Boston Museum of Fine Arts, 1908, and with Bourdelle in Paris, 1909–11. Lives in Buffalo

96 ABANDONED, 1927. *Bronze*
Private Collection, New York

97 TORSO, 1927. *Bronze*
Private Collection, New York

98 HEAD OF CHINESE WOMAN, 1928. *Bronze*
Private Collection, New York

99 HALLELUJAH, 1929. *Bronze*
Private Collection, New York

100 NEGRESS, 1930. *Bronze*
Private Collection, New York

101 PORTRAIT OF MRS. WOLCOTT, 1930. *Bronze*
Private Collection, New York

*102 HEAD OF KATHARINE CORNELL, 1930. *Bronze*
Private Collection, New York

103 PORTRAIT OF FRANCIS BANGS, 1930. *Bronze*
Private Collection, New York

GASTON LACHAISE

Born in Paris in 1882. Studied at Ecole des Beaux-Arts under Gabriel Jules Thomas. Lives in New York

104 WOMAN, 1912. *Bronze*
Collection John A. Dunbar, New York

*105 HEAD, 1922. *Bronze*
Collection Mrs. Charles J. Liebman, New York

106 WOMAN WALKING, 1922. *Bronze*
Private Collection, New York

107 SEATED WOMAN, 1924. *Bronze*
Collection Miss Marjorie Patterson, New York

107A TORSO. *Bronze*
Collection Weyhe Gallery, New York

108 HEAD, 1925. *Nickel*
Collection Kraushaar Galleries, New York

109 SLEEPING SEA GULL, 1925. *Alabaster*
Collection Kraushaar Galleries, New York

110 DOLPHIN FOUNTAIN, 1925. *Bronze*
Collection Kraushaar Galleries, New York

111 MASK, 1925. *Nickel*
Collection John F. Kraushaar, New York

112 PENGUIN, 1925. *Bronze*
Collection Mrs. W. Murray Crane, New York

113 LA MONTAGNE. *Bronze*
Collection Weyhe Gallery, New York

113A WOMAN, 1926. *Bronze*
Collection Paul Rosenfeld, New York

114 JOHN MARIN, 1927. *Bronze*
Collection Weyhe Gallery, New York

115 MAN, 1930
Collection the Artist

ROBERT LAURENT

Born in Concarneau, France, in 1890. Studied with Hamilton Easter Field and Maurice Sterne. Lives in New York

116 HEAD, 1926. *Alabaster*
Collection Downtown Gallery, New York

117 HEAD OF MIMI, 1927. *Plaster*
Collection the Artist

118 STANDING FIGURE, 1927. *Wood*
Collection Downtown Gallery, New York

119 RECLINING NUDE, 1927. *Alabaster*
Collection The Brooklyn Museum of Art, Brooklyn

*120 SEATED FIGURE, 1928. *Alabaster*
Collection John A. Dunbar, New York

121 STANDING FIGURE, 1930. *Bronze*
Collection Downtown Gallery, New York

DUDLEY VAIL TALCOTT

Born in Hartford, Connecticut, in 1899. Studied very briefly at Yale School of Fine Arts, 1919. Paris, 1921–25. Scandinavia and subartic regions, 1924–29. Lives at present in New York

122 SIX-DAY CYCLIST, 1926. *Bronze*
Collection the Artist

123 CHILD'S RESTAURANT WAITRESS, 1928. *Wood*
Collection the Artist

*124 WRESTLER, 1929. *Aluminum*
Collection the Artist

125 WOMAN WITH A WOODEN SPOON, 1929. *Tin*
Collection the Artist

126 GENEROUS GIRL, 1930. *Plaster*
Collection Murdock Pemberton, New York

WILLIAM ZORACH

Born in Russia in 1887. Studied at the National Academy of Design in New York, and in Paris. Lives in New York

127 BABY, 1918. *Bronze*
Collection Downtown Gallery, New York

128 KIDDY KAR, 1923. *Rosewood*
Collection Downtown Gallery, New York

*129 WOMAN, *about* 1924. *Lignum vitae.*
Collection Frank Crowninshield, New York

130 HEAD OF A CHILD, 1924. *Brass*
Collection Downtown Gallery, New York

131 PANELS, 1925. *Brazilian walnut*
Collection Downtown Gallery, New York

132 CHILD AND CAT, 1926. *Tennessee marble*
Collection Downtown Gallery, New York

133 PORTRAIT OF ARTIST'S WIFE, 1926. *Tennessee marble*
Collection Downtown Gallery, New York

134 SEATED FIGURE, 1930. *Bluestone*
Collection Downtown Gallery, New York

ILLUSTRATIONS

BEAL 1

FISHERMAN'S DAUGHTER, 1930. *24 x 18 inches*
Collection Kraushaar Galleries, New York

5 BURLIN

HORSES IN STABLE, *about* 1928. 30 x 38½ *inches*

Collection Mrs. M. deSilver, New York

CANADÉ 8

THE ARTIST'S FAMILY, *about* 1924. *29½ x 21½ inches*

Collection Weyhe Gallery, New York

12 CARLES

Calla Lilies, 1927

Collection Harry Sundheim, Philadelphia

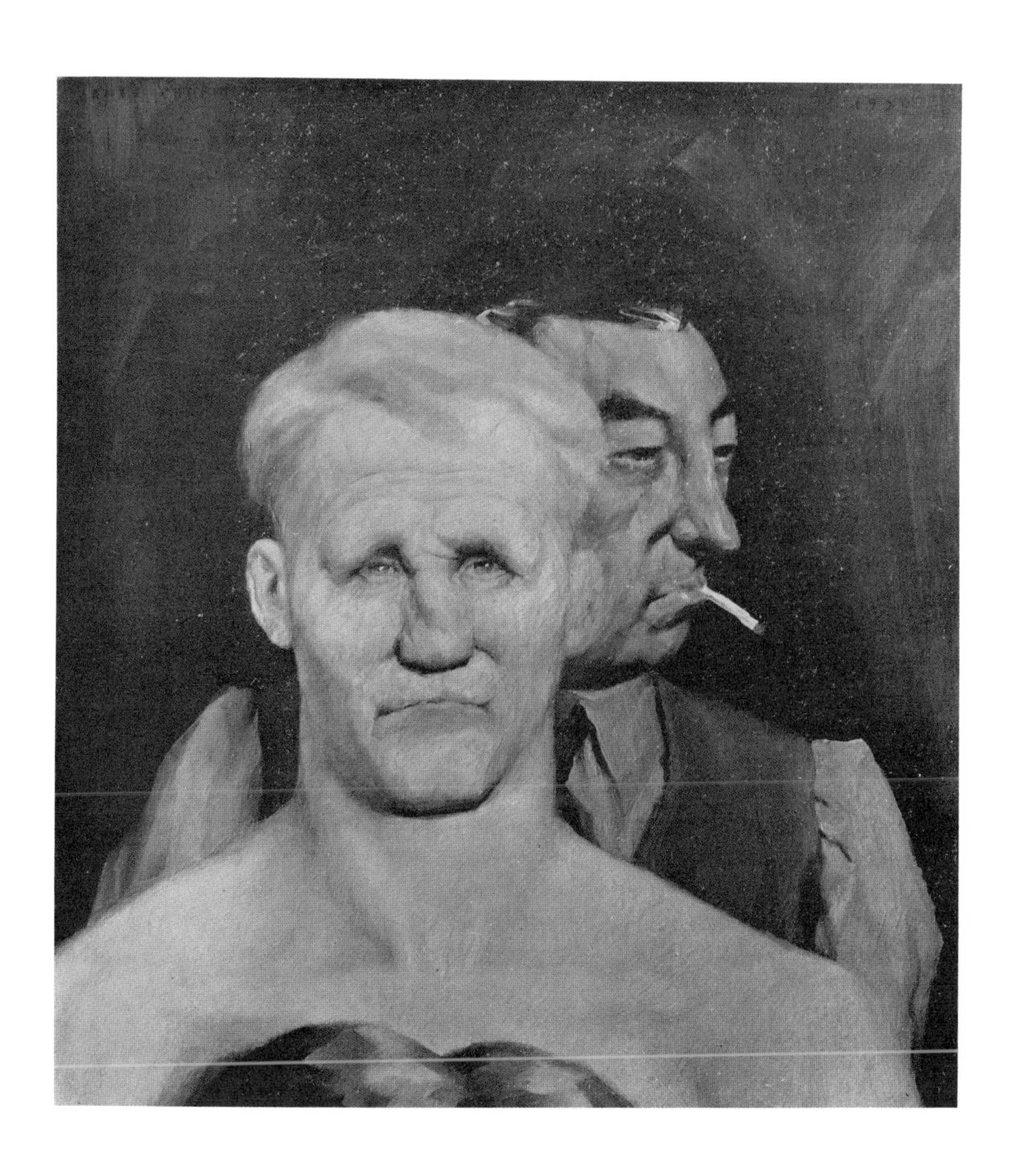

CHAPIN 15

BOXER AND HIS MANAGER, 1930. *21 x 91 inches*

Collection Frank K. M. Rehn Gallery, New York

16 CLIVETTE

JUNGLE ARGUMENT, *46 x 36 inches*

Collection Gustave Nassauer, New York

DASBURG 20

Poppies. *40 x 26 inches*

Collection Mr. and Mrs. Jay H. Barnum, Norwalk, Connecticut

24 DAVIS

SUMMER LANDSCAPE, 1930. *42 x 29½ inches*
Collection Downtown Gallery, New York

DOUGHERTY 27

SHADOWED MESA, 1930. *36 x 48 inches*

Collection the Artist

28 DOVE

DISTRACTION, 1929. *22 x 30 inches*

Collection An American Place, New York

DUBOIS 33

CAFÉ BREAKFAST, 1929. *36⅛ x 32 inches*

Collection Kraushaar Galleries, New York

35 FIENE

RAZING BUILDINGS, 49TH STREET, 1930. *26 x 36 inches*

Collection Frank K. M. Rehn Gallery, New York

FRIEDMAN 38

WHITE PONY, 1928. *14 x 19½ inches*

Collection Mrs. Charles J. Liebman, New York

40 GLACKENS
Dream Ride, 1923. *48 x 54 inches*
Collection Kraushaar Galleries, New York

HARTLEY 44

GRAPES, 1927. *20 x 23¾ inches*

Collection Phillips Memorial Gallery, Washington

46 HASSAM

SPRING IN WEST 78TH STREET, 1905
Private Collection, New York

KANE 48

HOMESTEAD. *24 x 27 inches*

Collection the Artist

52 KANTOR

Out of the Window, 1930. *42 x 32 inches*

Collection Frank K. M. Rehn Gallery, New York

KNATHS 54

COCK AND GLOVE, 1927. *35 x 26 inches*
Collection Phillips Memorial Gallery, Washington

59 KOPMAN

LANDSCAPE, 1930. *23 x 36 inches*

Collection J. B. Neumann, New York

KROLL 62

Folly Cove, 1930. *26 x 42 inches*
Collection Frank K. M. Rehn Gallery, New York

63 LAUFMAN

LANDSCAPE, 1930. *28½ x 39¼ inches*

Collection the Artist

LUKS 67

ELEANOR, 1927. *30 x 25 inches*

Collection Frank K. M. Rehn Gallery, New York

69 McFEE

LEAVES, 1927. *30 x 30 inches*

Collection Edward W. Root, Clinton, New York

ROBINSON 73

SERMON ON THE MOUNT, 1926. *60 x 96 inches*

Collection Eugene Schoen, Inc., New York

74 SCHNAKENBERG

STILL-LIFE WITH A RED BANDANA, 1929. 30 1/8 x 32 *inches*

Collection Kraushaar Galleries, New York

SHEELER 80

American Landscape, 1930. 24 x 31 *inches*
Collection the Artist

83 SPENCER

WHITE FACTORY, 1929. *20 x 25¾ inches*

Collection Daniel Gallery, New York

TACK 84

LARGO, 1928. *44 x 35½ inches*
Collection Phillips Memorial Gallery, Washington

87 TOBEY

AMERICAN LANDSCAPE, 1928. *38 x 60 inches*

Collection the Artist

CALDER 90
Cow
Collection George D. Pratt, Jr., Bridgewater, Connecticut

94 DIEDERICH

Wrestlers

Collection Downtown Gallery

GLENNY 102

Head of Katharine Cornell, 1930

Private Collection, New York

105 LACHAISE
HEAD
Collection Mrs. Charles J. Liebman, New York

LAURENT 120

SEATED FIGURE, 1928

Collection John A. Dunbar, New York

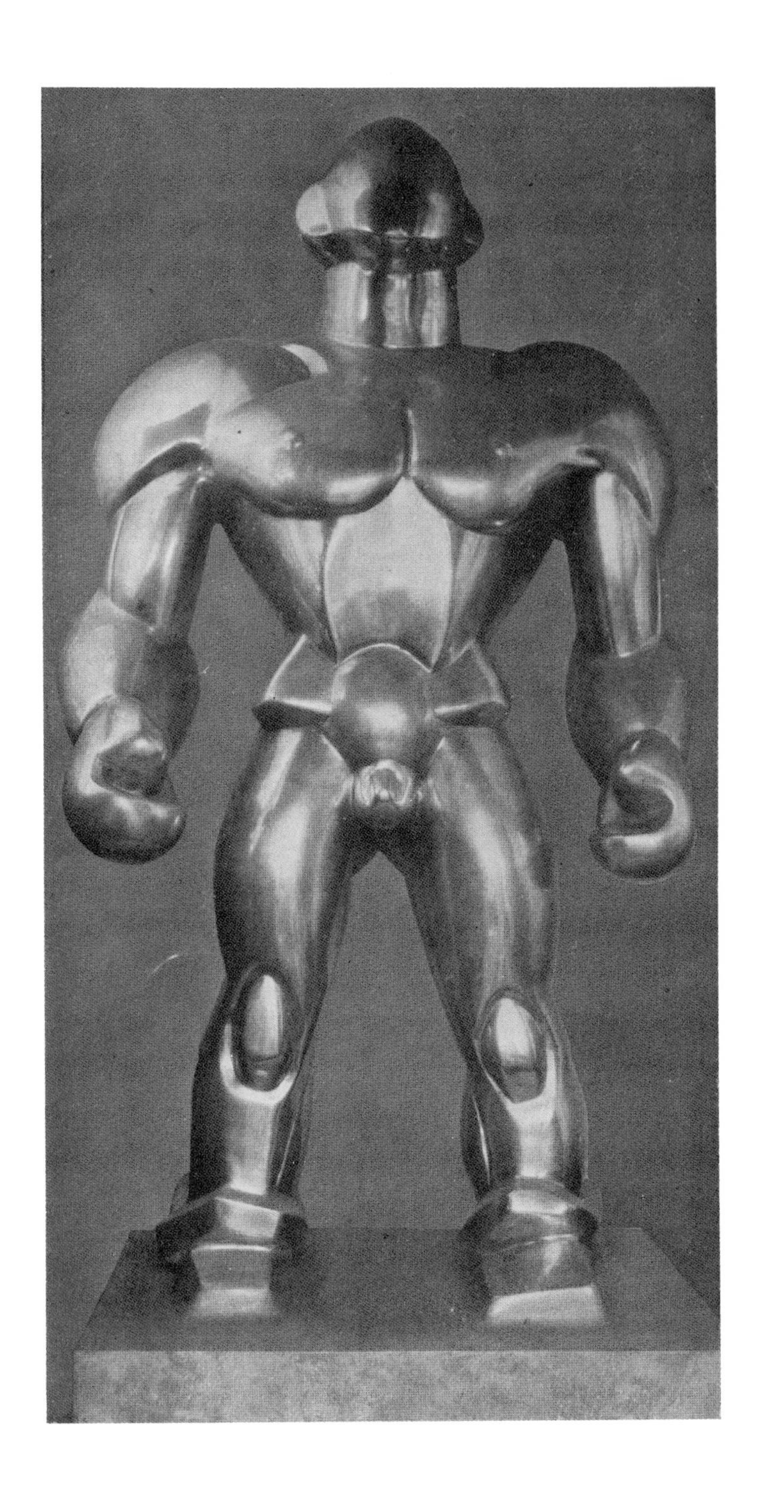

124 TALCOTT

WRESTLER, 1929

Collection the Artist

ZORACH 129

Woman, *about* 1924

Collection Frank Crowninshield, New York

ONE THOUSAND COPIES OF THIS CATALOG WERE
PRINTED FOR THE TRUSTEES OF THE MUSEUM OF
MODERN ART, BY THE PLANDOME PRESS OF NEW
YORK, DECEMBER SECOND, NINETEEN THIRTY

MURALS BY AMERICAN PAINTERS AND PHOTOGRAPHERS

NEW YORK :: 11 WEST FIFTY-THIRD STREET
MUSEUM OF MODERN ART

FOREWORD

STIMULATED in part by Mexican achievement, in part by recent controversy and current opportunity, American interest in mural decoration has increased astonishingly during the past year. Further to develop this interest and particularly to encourage American artists to study the possibilities of this medium of artistic expression, the Advisory Committee of the Museum has organized the present Exhibition.

Some sixty-five American painters and photographers, few of whom have made their reputation as mural designers, were invited to submit examples of their work. In order to approximate the difficulties of an actual commission, each artist was asked to design a horizontal composition in three parts, the whole study to measure twenty-one inches high by four feet wide. One section of the study was to be carried through to completion on a large panel to measure seven feet high by four feet wide. Any practicable medium was permissible. The subject was to be some aspect of "The Post-War World."

No other restrictions were placed upon the artists. The subject matter, its interpretation and the technique used are entirely the artist's own choice. The Committee has undertaken to make no selection among the pictures submitted, and no judgments are passed upon the relative merits of the themes chosen by the artists.

While the Exhibition will interest the general public, it is hoped that architects and others responsible for the selection of mural designers will study these paintings and photographs with special reference to the possibilities of beautifying future American buildings through the greater use of mural decoration.

The Advisory Committee, which was charged by the Museum with full responsibility for the organization and presentation of the Exhibition, wishes to thank the artists who have contributed their work. Thanks are also due to Mr. Julien Levy, who has generously given direction to the photomural section.

For the Advisory Committee,

NELSON ROCKEFELLER,
Chairman

LINCOLN KIRSTEIN,
Chairman, Exhibition Committee and Director of the Exhibition.

ADVISORY COMMITTEE OF THE MUSEUM OF MODERN ART

MISS ELIZABETH BLISS
MRS. PORTER CHANDLER
MISS ELIZABETH CLARK
MICHAEL CUYPERS
JOHN A. DUNBAR
MISS ETHEL HAVEN
PHILIP JOHNSON
LINCOLN KIRSTEIN
MRS. D. PERCY MORGAN, JR.
MRS. JAMES B. MURPHY
MRS. CHARLES S. PAYSON
NELSON A. ROCKEFELLER, *Chairman*
MRS. CHARLES H. RUSSELL
MRS. HOWARD J. SACHS
JAMES J. SWEENEY
E. M. M. WARBURG

Associate Members

MR. & MRS. JOHN NICHOLAS BROWN
MRS. WILLIAM F. C. GARTHWAITE
MISS DOROTHY STURGES
JOHN WALKER, III

MURAL PAINTING

ORIGINS AND DEVELOPMENT

THE decoration of walls by means of mural painting is as old as the stupendous bisons in the palaeolithic caves of Altamira, but the intention and function of mural painting has constantly changed. Prehistoric man recorded the giant bulls either as aid to an increase of power in their hunt or as some magic ward against the perils of famine, without much idea of making their caverns more "attractive." The byzantine mosaics of Hagia Sophia and Ravenna are symbols of dogma and walls of incandescent praise. Giotto's amethyst frescoes in Padua praise Christ the man and His mother, confirming the tradition for the decoration of wall surfaces in the West. As the Christian religion became more and more personalized, and abstract symbols of the Scripture took on everyday Florentine concreteness, mural painting shifted from its pure hieratic sobriety into the domestic academies of Benozzo Gozzoli and Ghirlandajo. The secularizing of the walls followed the popularizing of the Church, and people began to be satisfied with walls which were merely decorative backgrounds, a more congenially rich atmosphere against which to live. The element of praise and testimony was diminished and free decoration, the synthetic use of vegetable forms and fantastic classical fragments in Pompeian combinations culminated in Raphael's Villa Madama and marked the emergence of that bastard form of adornment—interior decoration.

THE PLACE FOR MURALS

Mural painting, when used as an integral part of interior architecture, produces an atmosphere of increasing richness. The walls may vibrate with the fluid expression of a pictorial and dramatic background, an intense if subdued shuttling of the fabric of a lyrical design which can enhance in its increasing beauty, the breathing of the men who take this background as their home. White walls are as fair as painted ones, but there are certain casual rooms of ceremony or leisure where an organic decoration is as necessary as the sheltering roof. One remembers the Piccolomini Library in Sienna and the ballroom that Rubens created for Marie di Medici. A blank wall suits a cloister, but in a monumental vaulted hall, or in a room of state, the blankness merely refers to the blank imaginations of the men who conceived it.

DIFFICULTIES AND OBJECTIONS

Architects have often been reluctant to accept mural painting as an essential or even as a desirable element in their interiors. Most of their objections to mural painting come from the fact that in the past too many rooms designed as bare boxes with a cornice, were thereafter delivered into the hands of a mural painter. Perhaps the room was inherently unsuited for his painting. Hence the certain discrepancies in scale which could never be resolved even by skillful painters. Often the murals were more important than the architecture of the room which enclosed them, as the Vatican Stanze or the Arena Chapel at Padua, or the Ministry of Education in Mexico City, the colonnades of which enclose the fine Riveras. The disadvantages of mural painting in public buildings are always cited more glibly than their advantages, but architects often forget that there are comparatively few rooms in the world which were designed to be decorated by specific works. The Scuola di S. Rocco in Venice, by Tintoretto, is a good example of one which was so planned.

It is to a great extent the responsibility of our architects whether the future of mural painting will be black or white. If the intention of the architect is clear, the painter can freely fulfill his commands. All the other objections to wall decoration can then be summarily disposed of. Architects, eager to delegate the responsibility for their chill marble halls have expressed the fear that if a painter is set loose he will "destroy the surface of the wall, and make the room look smaller," as if the first were a misfortune and the second made any difference. However, in those two objections can be found the root of the great restrictions from which mural painting too long has suffered.

FUNCTION AND MEDIUM

Wall decoration is perforce applied upon the surface of the wall. It is not bas-relief. Nevertheless, suggestions of an enlarged atmosphere can be obtained without having the painting stand out from the walls. Masaccio did it immemorially; so to a lesser degree have Rubens and Rivera. Tiepolo, in a miracle of exuberance, used his wall as a screen of paint and pushed his people infinitely out into the blue and straw-pale sky. Somehow our architects have a Puritanical heritage which arbitrarily states that piercing a wall is a deceit; that the wall must be maintained in the sincerity of its honest flat surface. They invoke the name of Puvis de Chavannes as a shibboleth and proceed to commission state capitols, railroad stations, banks and boardrooms, with weak blue and white echoes of Puvis' skim-milk shadows of the faded frescos of Florence. The enlargement of a room's atmosphere, whether accomplished by linear or aerial perspective, should not necessarily be deplored for its daring, but rather appreciated as an injection of excitement into the vapid echoes that irritate most of our painted rooms.

For the history of mural painting in North America is not a particularly inspiriting record. We have only a few brilliant exceptions to gainsay the tedium of academic memories of Venice and Rome, thinned out with the discreet draperies of the Columbian Exhibition of 1892. John LaFarge's great bay in the Church of the Ascension on Fifth Avenue is perhaps the most distinguished religious painting of the Nineteenth Century; while, recalling Perugino and Raphael, it never depends on a stylization of their superficial attitude. John Singer Sargent's vault and walls in the Boston Public Library have a richness of texture and a mesh of imaginative iconography that is unique in this country in its appropriateness to the locale. The Columbian Exposition, the Congressional Library in Washington, the Boston Public Library, the Appellate Courts Building of New York, the State Capitol at Albany, and scores of other public buildings were filled with pompous echoes of Venice and Rome, or genteel costume illustrations.

MURALS IN THE UNITED STATES

THE NINETEENTH CENTURY

The Twentieth Century American Academy at Rome has produced a tradition of mural painting which means "murals" to most contemporary American architects. To say that they are academic hardly disposes of them. Ghirlandajo was academic and so is Rivera, insomuch as every piece of their work conforms to a more or less presupposed attitude of competent, formularized and rather abstracted rigidity. Each new panel is handled in the same intelligent and workmanlike way. There is none of the risky daring that might result in a "brilliant failure." The School of Rome is academic but it is the academy of a particularly strangulated, debased and flat archaisticism—the dilution of models already diluted. Far more significant are the murals by Thomas Benton in the New School for Social Research, and by Boardman Robinson in the Kauffman Department Store in Pittsburgh.

THE SCHOOL OF ROME

Perhaps it is the problem of iconography which has crippled our artists. Robbed of the symbols of Christian dogma we have tried to rely on an imposed set of civic values. "Freedom," "Justice," "The Melting Pot," "The Spirit of Liberty," are as devoid of real meaning as the ideas which they attempt to convey. Sargent's assumption of a frankly literary background, in the Boston Public Library, is far more satisfactory. Mexico has the advantage of a rich religious legend of Aztec, Conquistador and Socialist revolutions from which to draw. We too have the backgrounds of an exciting past, but without any real symbolic figures. The pioneering West, New Bedford's whaling and our mechanical ingenuity are subject matter enough, providing we find artists with an organized imagination. Raphael had the ordered hierarchies of Aristotle to

ICONOGRAPHY AND SUBJECT MATTER

help arrange the grouping of his figures in the "School of Athens." We have the anarchy of the tabloids, industrial implements and passing people in the street, without any spiritual values to integrate them into a lyric expression of our contemporaneity.

But whether or not we have universal symbols we have walls, and for the present event, this is more important. Easel painting has become ingrown, inorganic. The accidental vision on the private wall, bought by whatever patron happens along, is as unsatisfactory to the ambition of an artist occupied with all the potentials of a permanent appeal as with the great mass of people who, if given such a chance, would look at paintings.

ECONOMIC CONSIDERATIONS

Our building methods, our subservience to the speed which property must realize in order to triple its value are not very propititious to mural painting, or even to architecture. The marble companies can offer their flat, chilly slabs. These immaculate vitreous panels are shot up to the lobby ceiling quickly and neatly, with gratitude for their lack of upkeep and no thought of their lack of warmth or imagination. It goes without saying that if there were more interest on the part of the architects there would be more mural painting in America. It has taken Mexico to show us the way.

MEDIUMS AND TECHNICS

The scratch with a bone knife on the wall of a cave which outlined the antlers of a prehistoric stag may have been the first means by which the decorations of walls were realized. Later the rock's surface was stained with earth colors. The Egyptians incised their hieratic silhouettes into their sandstone walls and filled in the shapes with flat fields of color which have mostly disappeared. Perhaps the Cretans used *buon fresco* for the first time. Real fresco, the process of painting in earth colors on a wet plaster wall which incorporates the pigment into the very fabric of the building, is the most permanent and respected of mural mediums and has been used by great decorators from the days of the Tauromachies of Knossos, through Giotto and Michelangelo to Rivera and Orozco. The Byzantines inlaid bits of glass and stone to form mosaics upon their walls and the gothic cathedral builders created, in piercing their walls, a flat decoration of transparent pieced and colored windows. Since the Renaissance, for practical reasons such as speed and portability, mural artists have chosen to paint in oil on canvas panels that could be applied to the wall by nails or coatings of white lead, and removed if the building was to perish. Recently, especially in the schools of Mexico City, Harvard and Fontainbleau, there has been a renaissance of interest in true fresco.

The contemporary enthusiasm for synthetic materials has left its mark upon mural painting and there is a broad field for the artist who now wishes to create new modes of expression for himself. The factors of permanence at low cost of upkeep, ease of installation and high speed of creation are preëminent in the eyes of commissioning architects. In the present exhibition not only the older methods of buon fresco and oil on canvas have been used, but also wax encaustic, egg and watercolor tempera on various wood and pressed-wood boards, and even the innovation of transparent panels of chalked celluloid welded between two plates of transparent glass.

NEW METHODS AND MATERIALS

LINCOLN KIRSTEIN

PHOTO-MURALS

THE photographer is particularly well equipped to meet the problems of mural decoration as posed by the modern architect and builder. The photographers in the present exhibition were invited only three weeks before the preliminary sketches were due. In the time elapsing between filing the plans for a building and the final preparation of the wall, the enlargements would be executed, projected, developed, fixed, backed with canvas, and eventually mounted, or hung as wall-paper is hung, glazed with a transparent varnish by the house painter. The cost of execution for such murals would be minimum. When it is considered that the life of a modern building is usually something under seventy-five years, it is often desirable to secure the best possible decoration with the least expenditure. Furthermore, the photo-murals are mounted on canvas so that they may be stripped easily from the walls to be installed in a new location, or renewed every several years with decoration of immediate topical interest for our shifting modern life. Thus the new medium satisfies at once three primary requisites of modern building: speed, economy, and flexibility.

The use of photographs for wall decoration was made possible only recently by the perfecting of a sensitized paper in large sheets, which would reproduce,

ORIGIN OF PHOTO-MURALS

when exposed to a projected image from a negative, the original tones with the original scale of values in enlarged size. This facility was extensively employed by movie directors in Hollywood as an economy to replace the painted back-drop, and by interior decorators to enlarge drawings, old engravings, etc. The history of photo-mural repeats in a condensed span of time the history of photography, first as a primitive in the service of economic realism, then self-consciously imitating painting and the graphic arts; yesterday using the actual photographic medium as basis for expression, and only today in this present exhibition inviting recognized artists in the medium to study the new problem and contribute their projects.

PHOTO-MURALS AS DECORATION

A good photo-mural is not merely the mechanical enlargement of a small photograph. The enlarged mural is a new and independent production, and the photographer who does not visualize in advance the final scale of his picture will usually be surprised and dismayed by the results. Not only must all the precepts of the mural painter be kept well in mind, but additional and unsuspected difficulties arise. For the original photograph may completely lose its identity when enlarged, the essential forms becoming almost unrecognizable when dissipated over a greater area. Conversely an unimportant shape in the small photograph may gain impressive dramatic force by progressive exaggeration. It is difficult to stretch a single, simple photograph over a large space and maintain interest, but it is dangerous to enlarge a complicated negative, as the photographer has little control over the minor bits in his picture, and just as the peculiar virtues of a photograph are dramatized by enlargement, so are any faults equally exaggerated. One solution may be the use of what is called "montage". . . the cutting out and reassembling of parts from separate pictures. In this method there is always the chance that the result will appear disjointed and arbitrary.

As there exists no traditional solution to aid the photographer past these primary difficulties, an attempt has been made to divide the problem so that each photographer concentrates in the present exhibition more or less on one particular aspect of the photo-mural (while they must all answer one question in common: what can the photograph present that is not better rendered in paint?)

JULIEN LEVY

MURAL PAINTINGS

Large panels measure seven feet high by four feet wide; the small studies, illustrated at bottom of each page, measure about 21 inches high by 48 inches wide.

BECKER

Maurice Becker, painter and cartoonist. Born in Russia in 1889. Arrived in U. S. A. in 1891. Educated in New York public schools, and in a lithographer's studio, 1907. Studied under Robert Henri and Homer Boss, 1908-15. Cartoonist, 1911-20. Exhibited in the Armory Show, New York, 1913. One-man shows in New York at J. B. Neumann Gallery, 1924-31; Whitney Studio Club, 1924-28; Delphic Studios, 1930; New School for Social Research, 1932.

Large panel

Tribute to Einstein
based on left-hand section of Study

Study for three-part composition (below)

left: A Tribute to Einstein
center: The Spirit of Peace
right: The Victory of the Conscientious Objectors

Medium: Oil on canvas

BERLANDINA

Jane Berlandina (Mrs. Henry Howard), painter and lithographer. Born in Nice, France, 1898. Educated at the Ecole National des Arts Décoratifs, Nice, 1914-19. Fresco painting with Paul Baudoin, Nice, 1915. Paris, 1919-28. One-man shows at the Brummer Galleries, New York, 1929-30. Georgette Passedoit Gallery, 1931-32. At present a lecturer on Modern French Art at the University of California.

Large panel (illustrated at right)

Radio Publicity
based on central panel of Study

Study for three-part composition (below)

left: Radio Music
center: Radio Publicity
right: Radio News

Medium: Tempera on presswood panel.

BIBERMAN

Edward Biberman, painter. Born in Philadelphia, 1904. Graduated from the University of Pennsylvania, 1924. Studied at the Pennsylvania Academy of Fine Arts under McCarter and Carles, 1924-26. Worked alone in Europe, 1926-29. One-man shows, Galerie Zak, Paris, 1929; Neue Kunsthandlung, Berlin, 1929; Montross Gallery, New York 1931, 32; Arts Club of Chicago, 1932. Represented in the Pennsylvania Academy of Fine Arts (John Lambert Purchase Prize, 1931).

Large panel (illustrated at left)

Bodies of Men and Fabric of Building
based on right-hand section of Study

Study for three-part composition (below)

Genesis of the Skyscraper

left: Beginning of the Concept
center: Human Hands and Steel
right: Bodies of Men and Fabric of the Building

Medium: Large panel, oil on gesso grounded presswood; study, oil on canvas.

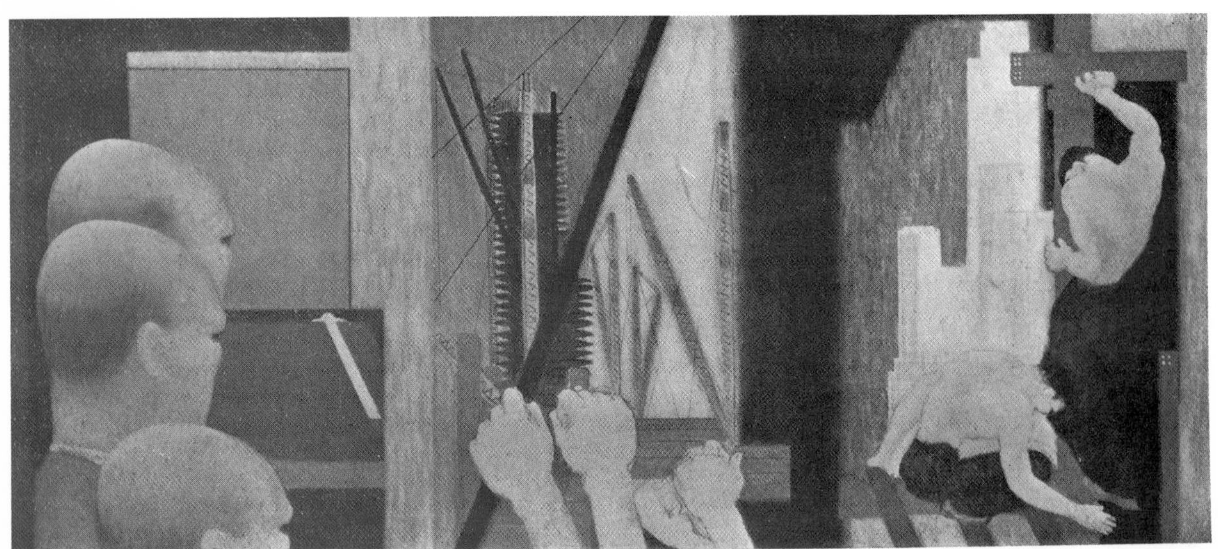

BIDDLE

George Biddle, painter and lithographer. Born in Philadelphia, 1885. Studied in the Pennsylvania Academy of Fine Arts, in Paris, and in Munich. Served in the War and spent two years in a Polynesian village. Lived in the American West and Southwest and in Mexico. Represented in the permanent collections of the Pennsylvania Academy of Fine Arts, and the Art Institute of Chicago. One-man shows at the Frank K. M. Rehn Gallery, 1928, '29, '30.

Large panel (illustrated at right)

Plowing
based on central section of Study

Study for three-part composition (below)

Labor—Black and White

Medium: Large panel, true fresco (watercolor on wet plaster); study, tempera on gesso-grounded wood.

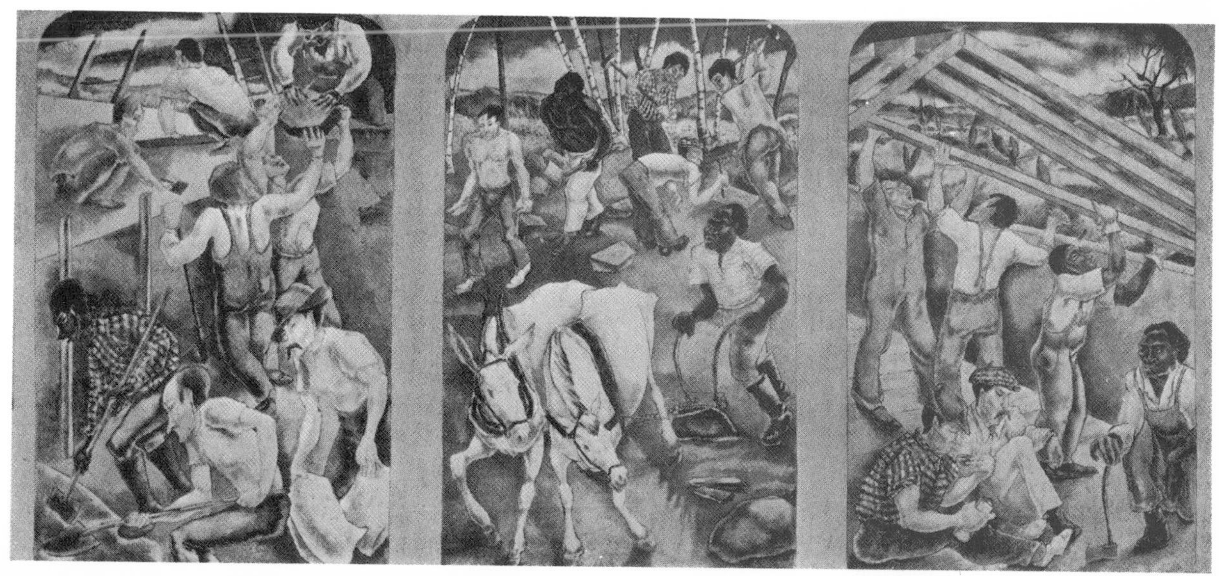

BILLINGS

Henry Billings, painter and mural decorator. Born, New York City, 1901. Studied, Art Students' League, 1918-20. First one-man show at the Daniel Gallery, 1928. Exhibition of sample murals in relief and metal, Squibb Building, New York, 1932. Represented in the Gallery of Living Art, New York University, and the Whitney Museum of American Art.

Large panel (illustrated at left)

Electrical Research
based on central section of Study

Study for three-part composition (below)

Electricity in Modern Life

left: Source of Electrical Power
center: Electrical Research
right: Electrical Amusements, particularly Television

Medium: Oil paint and metal leaf upon prepared wood.

BOUCHÉ

Louis Bouché, painter and mural decorator. Born in New York, 1896. Studied in Paris at La Grande Chaumière and L'Ecole des Beaux-Arts, 1910-15, and at the Art Students' League, New York, 1915-16. One-man show at the Valentine Gallery, 1932. At present the Assistant Director of the New York School of Interior Decoration. Represented in the permanent collection of the Gallery of Living Art, New York University, the Whitney Museum of American Art, and the Phillips Memorial Gallery, Washington.

Large panel (illustrated at right)

Locomotive Engine
based on detail of central section of Study

Study for three-part composition (below)

The Apotheosis of Transportation

left: Automobile and Hydraulic Traction
center: Locomotive Engine
right: Shipping

Medium: Oil on canvas.

COLEMAN

Glenn Coleman, painter and lithographer. Born, Springfield, Ohio, 1887. Came to New York, 1900. Studied with Robert Henri and Everett Shinn. One of the first Independents. Exhibited in the Armory Show, New York, 1913; made drawings for the old *Masses*. One-man show, Downtown Gallery, New York, 1931, etc. Represented in the permanent collections of the Luxembourg, Brooklyn Museum, Newark Museum, Whitney Museum of American Art, the Gallery of Living Art, New York University, and the Phillips Memorial Gallery, Washington.

Large panel (illustrated at left)

The Old and the New
based on central section of Study

Study for three-part composition (below)

Manhattan; the Old and the New

Medium: Oil on canvas.

JAMES E. DAVIS

James Edward Davis, painter. Born in Clarksburg, West Virginia, 1901. Was graduated from Princeton University, 1923. Pupil of André L'hôte, Paris, 1924-25, 1926-27. One-man shows in New York at S. P. R. Galleries, 1930, 1932.

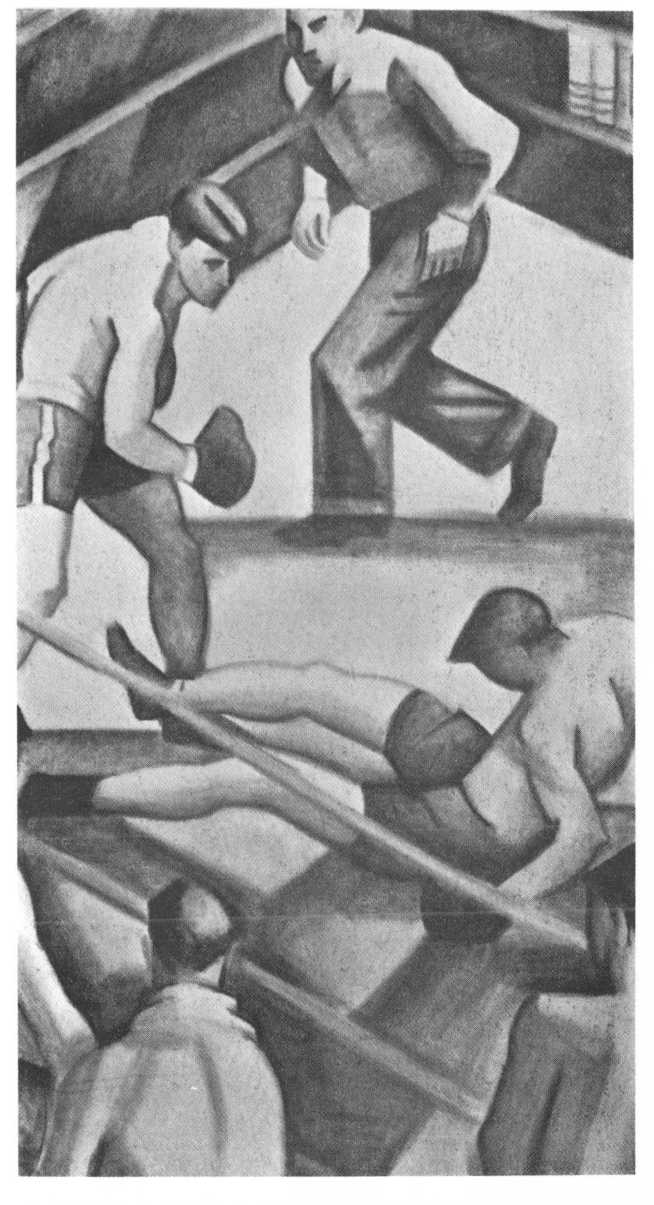

Large panel (illustrated at right)

Boxing
based on central section of Study

Study for three-part composition (below)

Sport

left: Swimming
center: Boxing
right: Track and Field

Medium: Pastel on celluloid welded between two sheets of unbreakable glass giving a permanent and easily cleaned surface. (The large panel is in pastel on tracing paper.)

STUART DAVIS

Stuart Davis, painter and lithographer. Born in Philadelphia, 1892. Studied with Robert Henri, 1910-12. Exhibited in the Armory Show, 1913. One-man show at the Whitney Club, 1920, '26, '29; Downtown Gallery, 1927, '31, '32. Represented in the Whitney Museum of American Art, Newark Museum, Los Angeles Museum, Phillips Memorial Gallery, Washington, and Pennsylvania Academy Gallery, Philadelphia. At present an instructor at the Art Students' League, New York.

Large panel (illustrated at left)

Abstract Vision of New York: a building, a derby hat, a tiger's head, and other symbols.

based on central section of Study

Study for three-part composition (below)

Abstract Vision of New York

Medium: Oil laid on canvas with palette knife.

EVERGOOD

Philip Evergood, painter and engraver. Born in New York, 1901. Educated at Eton College, Windsor, 1915-19, Trinity Hall, Cambridge, England, 1919-21. Studied art at the Slade School, London, and under Howard Thomas, sculptor, 1921-23; Art Students' League, New York, 1923-24; the Academie Julien, Paris, 1924; and at the British Academy, Rome, 1925. One-man shows in New York at the Dudensing Galleries, 1927; Montross Gallery, 1929.

Large panel (illustrated at right)

The Angel of Peace Offering the Fruit of Knowledge to the World
based on central section of Study

Study for three-part composition (below)

left: The Advance of Medicine and Agriculture
center: The Angel of Peace
right: Apotheosis of Ancient and Modern Learning

Medium: Oil on canvas.

FIENE

Ernest Fiene, painter, etcher, and lithographer. Born in the Rhineland, Germany, 1894. Educated at the National Academy of Design, 1915-19, and in etching and lithography at the Art Students' League, New York, 1924-25. At present an instructor in drawing, painting, and etching at the Westchester County Center. One-man shows in New York at Whitney Studio Club, 1923; Frank K. M. Rehn Gallery, 1926, '30, '31; The Downtown Gallery, 1928; and in Chicago at the Arts Club, 1930. Represented in the permanent collection of the Boston Museum of Fine Arts, the Phillips Memorial Gallery, Washington, the Newark, Los Angeles and San Francisco Museums, and the Whitney Museum of American Art.

Large panel (illustrated at left)

Aviation

based on left-hand section of Study

Study for three-part composition (below)

Mechanical Progress

left: Aviation

center: Television

right: Steel Structure

Medium: Tempera on gesso grounded wooden panels.

GASSNER

Mordi Gassner, painter and mural decorator. Born in New York, 1899. Educated at New York School of Fine and Applied Art under Howard Giles and Felicie Waldo Howells, 1916-19; Art Students' League, New York, 1918; Brooklyn Institute of Arts and Science, 1917-19. Exhibited in New York at Art Centre, 1928, and at the Brooklyn Museum, 1932 (June to October). Guggenheim Fellowship, 1928-30; worked in Florence.

Large panel

Abstract or Geometric Art
based on central section of Study

Study for three-part composition (below)

The Three Categories of Modernist Art

left: The Archaistic
center: The Mathematical Abstract
right: The Psychological

Medium: Oil on canvas.

YUN GEE

Yun Gee, painter and sculptor. Born in Canton, China, 1906. Studied painting under the Chinese master Chu, 1918-19. Came to San Francisco in 1921. Studied at the California Art School, 1923-25. Founded the Revolutionary Art Club, 1926. Left for Paris, 1927. One-man shows, Galerie Carmine, and Bernheim-Jeune. Returned to New York in 1930.

Large panel

Wheels: Industrial New York

Study for three-part composition (below)

left: Merry-Go-Round
center: Sun Bathers
right: Modern Apartment

Medium: Oil on canvas.

GELLERT

Hugo Gellert, painter and graphic artist. Born in Budapest, 1892. Studied at the National Academy of Design, New York, 1908-13. One-man shows in New York at the Kevorkian Galleries, 1923, and J. B. Neumann's, 1926. Draws for the *New Yorker*, the *New Masses*, and many other periodicals.

Large panel (completed too late for illustration)

Last Defenses of Capitalism
based on left-hand section of Study

Study for three-part composition (below)

The Triumph of Lenin

Medium: chalk on celotex sized with plaster

GOODMAN

Bertram Goodman, painter and mural decorator. Born in New York City, 1904. Studied drawing at the Art Students' League, 1923; with Mahonri Young, 1924; with Harry Wickey, 1925. Exhibited at the Brooklyn Museum, 1925-29; at the Art Institute of Chicago, 1931.

Large panel

Pneumatic Drilling
based upon right-hand section of Study

Study for three-part composition (below)

Makers of Skyscrapers

left: Riveting
center: Excavation
right: Pneumatic Drilling

Medium: Oil on canvas

GROPPER

William Gropper, painter, graphic artist and illustrator. Born in New York City, 1897. Studied under Robert Henri and George Bellows, 1912-14, and at the New York School of Fine and Applied Arts, under Howard Giles, 1918. Staff artist for *New York Tribune*, 1917-19, *World*, 1925-28, *Morning Freiheit*, 1922-32. Exhibited at Berkeley Museum, Berkeley, California, 1931; John Reed Club, New York, 1932; Decora Gallery, New York, 1932. Has illustrated seventeen books and written three. Represented in Museum of Modern Western Art, and Museum of the Revolution, Moscow, U. S. S. R.

Large panel

based on central section of Study

Study for three-part composition (below)

Class Struggle in America Since the War

Medium: large panel, oil on canvas; study, a photograph of drawings

HIRSCH

Stefan Hirsch, painter. Born in Nuremberg, Germany, of American parents, 1899. Studied in the University of Zurich, and with Hamilton Easter Field in Brooklyn. Represented in the Worcester Museum, Whitney Museum of American Art, Phillips Memorial Gallery, Washington, Preston Harrison Collection, Los Angeles, and the Field Foundation in Brooklyn. One-man shows in New York at the Bourgeois Galleries, and two at the Downtown Gallery in 1928 and 1930.

Large panel (illustrated at left)

The Builder at Work
based on detail of central section of

Study for three-part composition (below)

Tragedy of the Builder

Medium: Large panel, true fresco (watercolor on wet plaster); study.

KANTOR

Morris Kantor, painter and lithographer. Born in Russia, 1896. Came to the United States in 1909. Studied under Homer Boss, 1916-17. Exhibited at the Brummer Gallery, 1929. One-man shows at Rehn Gallery, New York, 1930, '32; Logan medal and First Prize, Chicago Art Institute, 1931. One-man show, Chicago Art Institute, 1932. Represented in permanent collection of the Chicago Art Institute, the Phillips Memorial Gallery, Washington, Whitney Museum of American Art, Gallery of Living Art, New York University.

Large panel (illustrated at right)

Union Square, New York
based on central section of Study

Study for three-part composition (below)

left: Airways
center: Union Square
right: New York Harbor

Medium: Oil on canvas

KNATHS

Karl Knaths, painter. Born in Eau Claire, Wisconsin, 1891. Graduate of the Art Institute, Chicago. One-man shows: Phillips Memorial Gallery, Washington, 1929; Daniel Gallery, New York, 1930; Downtown Gallery, New York, 1931; Phillips Memorial Gallery, Washington, 1931, where he is permanently represented as well as in the Gallery of Living Art, New York University.

Large panel

The Sea
based on right-hand section of Study

Study for three-part composition (below)

left: Architecture
center: Abstract Design
right: The Sea

Medium: Large panel, oil on canvas; Study, watercolor on celotex.

KOPMAN

Benjamin Kopman, painter and graphic artist. Born in Russia, 1887. Studied at the National Academy of Design. One-man shows in Chicago at the Thurber Galleries, 1920; in New York at the Weyhe Gallery, 1925; at J. B. Neumann's, 1929, '31. Represented in the Brooklyn Museum, the Philadelphia Academy, the Whitney Museum of American Art, and the Metropolitan Museum Print Room.

Large panel (illustrated at right)

Parade

based on central section of Study

Study for three-part composition (below)

Vision of the Militaristic State

Medium: Oil on cardboard.

LaFARGE

Thomas LaFarge, painter and mural decorator. Born in Paris, 1904, of American parents. Educated in Switzerland and at Harvard; Yale School of Fine Arts, 1923-24. Worked in collaboration with his father, Bancel LaFarge, on mural decorations, 1925-30. One-man shows in Boston, 1924, '26, '28, '31; in New York 1930, and in Washington, 1932.

Large panel (illustrated at left)

Man's Eye and Telescopic Television
based on central section of Study

Study for three-part composition (below)

Telescopic Television

left: God's Eye

center: Man's Eye and Telescopic Television

right: The Resulting Comprehension of the Universe

Medium: Large panel, wax encaustic on composition board; Study, tempera on gesso ground.

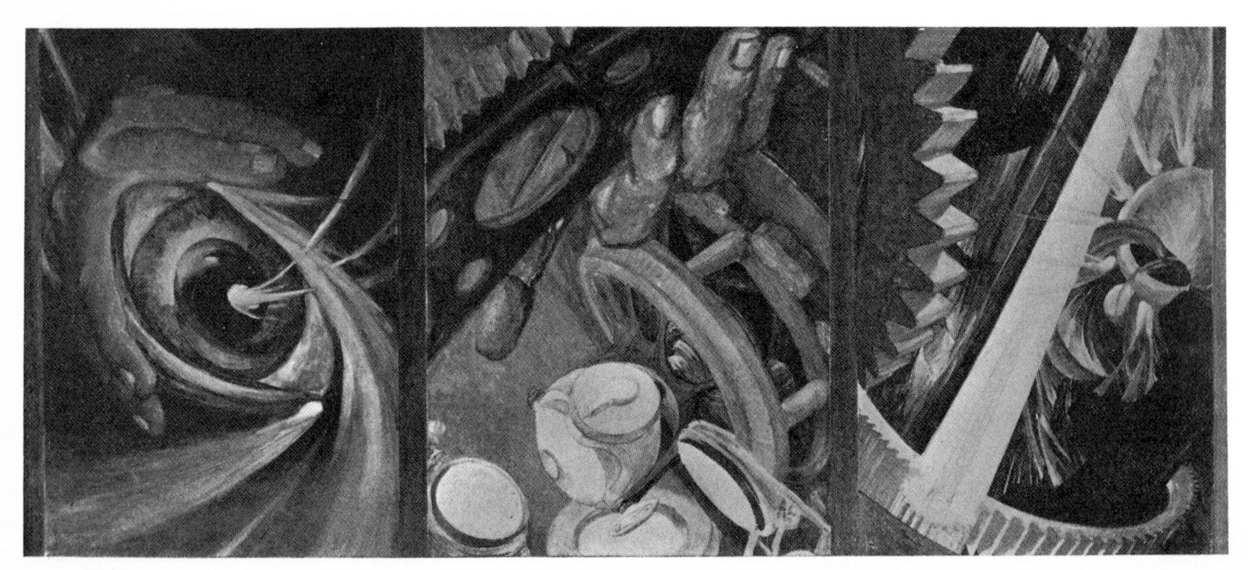

LANING

Edward Laning, painter. Born in Petersburg, Illinois, 1906. Studied at the Art Students' League, New York, 1926-30, chiefly under Kenneth Hayes Miller. Exhibited at the Dudensing Galleries at various times during the past two years. At present an instructor at the Art Students' League, New York.

Large panel

based on right-hand section of Study.

Study for three-part composition (below)

Broadway

Medium: Tempera on wood

LEWIS

Monty Lewis, painter and mural decorator. Born in Cardiff, South Wales, 1906. Educated at the Art Students' League, New York, 1924-27. Tiffany Foundation Fellowship, 1928. Worked with various mural painters, 1929. Guggenheim Fellowship, 1930. Eighteen months abroad, living in Florence over a year. Exhibited in New York at the G. R. D. Galleries, 1929, '30. One-man show at the Newhouse Galleries, 1932; Baltimore Museum of Art, 1932. Decorations in home of Philip Roosevelt, Oyster Bay, Long Island, 1929-30.

Large panel (illustrated at left)
based on detail of central section of Study

Study for three-part composition (below)
New York Holiday

Medium: Large panel, oil on paper; study, pencil on paper.

LITTLEFIELD

William Littlefield, painter and graphic artist. Born in Roxbury, Massachusetts, 1902. Educated at the Roxbury Latin School and Harvard College. In Paris, 1925-28. Folio of boxing lithographs published in Paris, 1928. One-man shows at John Becker Gallery, New York, 1931; Albright Gallery, Buffalo, 1931; Baltimore Museum of Art, 1931; Gordon Gallery, Detroit, 1931.

Large panel (illustrated at right)

Victory of Truth (David and Goliath)
based on left-hand section of Study

Study for three-part composition (below)

A Modern Allegory on Universal Symbols

left: Victory of Truth (David and Goliath)

center: Revelation (St. John and the Angel on the Island of Patmos)

right: Fraternity (David and Jonathan on the Eve of David's Victory over Goliath)

Medium: Mussini transparent oil glaze on canvas.

MARSH

Reginald Marsh, painter, etcher and illustrator. Born in Paris, 1898, of American parents, Educated at Lawrenceville School, 1926, and Yale University, 1920. Studied painting with Kenneth Hayes Miller, 1927-28. One-man shows at Frank Rehn Galleries, 1931, '32. Represented in the permanent collections of the Whitney Museum of American Art, the Metropolitan Museum of Art, etc.

Large panel (illustrated at left)
based on right-hand section of Study

Study for three-part composition (below)
Post-War America

Medium: Tempera on composition board.

MATULKA

Jan Matulka, painter and graphic artist. Born at Prague, Czecho-Slovakia, 1892. Came to the United States in 1907. Studied at the National Academy of Design, winning the Pulitzer Scholarship in Columbia University. He traveled over the United States, Mexico, Canada, and the Bahamas. To Paris in 1918. Returned to the United States in 1924 and has held one-man shows in New York at Columbia University, the Art Centre, and the Frank K. M. Rehn Gallery.

Large panel

Nudist Colony
based on a section of Study

Study for three-part composition (below)

Television
(Completed too late for illustration)

Medium: Oil on canvas.

NICOLAIDES

Kimon Nicolaides, painter. Born in Washington, D. C., 1892. Studied at the Art Students' League, New York, 1914-16. Exhibited at Bernheim-Jeune, Paris, 1922; Whitney Studio Club, 1922. At present an instructor at the Art Students' League, New York. Represented in the Whitney Museum of American Art.

Large panel (illustrated at left)
based on right-hand section of Study

Study for composition (below)

Manhattan Merry-Go-Round, a circular procession of wrestlers, New Yorkers, chorus girls, gangsters, etc., led by a jazz band.

Medium: large panel, color glazed over under painting of black and white.

O'KEEFFE

Georgia O'Keeffe, painter. Born in Sun Prairie, Wisconsin, 1887. Studied in the Chicago Art Institute under John Vanderpoel; later at the Art Students' League, New York, under Cox, Chase, and Mora. Yearly one-man exhibitions at Alfred Stieglitz' Gallery. Represented in the permanent collection of the Brooklyn Museum, The Barnes Foundation, the Whitney Museum of American Art, and the Phillips Memorial Gallery, Washington.

Large panel (illustrated at right)
based on central section of Study

Study for three-part composition (below)
Manhattan

Medium: Oil on canvas.

POOR

Henry Varnum Poor, painter and ceramic artist. Born in Kansas, 1888. Educated at Stanford University, 1910. Studied in London and Paris. First one-man show in San Francisco, 1917; in New York, at Kevorkian's, 1920. First pottery show at Montross, 1921. Pottery in permanent collections of the Metropolitan Museum of Art, New York; Art Institute of Chicago, San Francisco, etc.

Large panel (illustrated at left)

The Arts and Crafts
based on central section of Study

Study for three-part composition (below)

left: Home Life in the Country
center: The Arts and Crafts
right: The City

Medium: The Study is in glazed tile; the large panel, in true fresco (watercolor on wet plaster). The artist proposes to do murals in glazed tile.

REISMAN

Philip Reisman, painter and graphic artist. Born in Warsaw, Poland, 1904. Came to America at the age of four. Studied at the Art Students' League, New York, under Wallace Morgan and George Bridgeman, 1920-25. Illustrated for Collier's Weekly, 1926-27. Studied under Harry Wickey, 1927-29. Etchings in the permanent collections of the Bibliothèque Nationale, Paris, and the Metropolitan Museum of Art.

Large panel (illustrated at right)
based on central section of Study

Study for three-part composition (below)
The Post-War World

Medium: Tempera on wood.

SHAHN

Ben Shahn, painter and lithographer. Born in Russia, 1898. Apprenticeship as a lithographer, 1913-17. Academic education at New York University and the College of the City of New York. Studied at the National Academy of Design, 1925, '28-'29. One-man exhibitions at the Downtown Gallery, 1930, '32.

Large panel (illustrated at left)
based on right-hand section of Study

Study for three part composition (below)
The Passion of Sacco and Vanzetti

Medium: emulsion of oil and tempera on canvas sized with gesso and mounted on pressed wood

STERNE

Maurice Sterne, painter, sculptor and graphic artist. Born at Libau, Latvia, 1878. Studied art at Cooper Union 1893-94, National Academy of Design 1895-99. Paris 1904-07, Italy and Greece. Has spent much time in Italy and Dutch East Indies as well as in America. Represented in the Metropolitan Museum of Art; Boston Museum of Fine Arts; Carnegie Institute, Pittsburgh; Corcoran Gallery, Washington; Phillips Memorial Gallery, Washington; Art Institute of Chicago; Cleveland Museum of Art; Brooklyn Museum; Detroit Museum; Worcester Museum; Rhode Island School of Design; Tate Gallery, London; Berlin Museum; Wallraf-Richartz Museum; Museum of Cologne; Ulm Museum; Uffizi Gallery, Florence.

Large panel (completed too late for illustration)

Metal-Work
based on section of Study

Study for three-part composition (below)

Television

Agriculture
Textiles
Metal-Work

Medium: Oil on canvas.

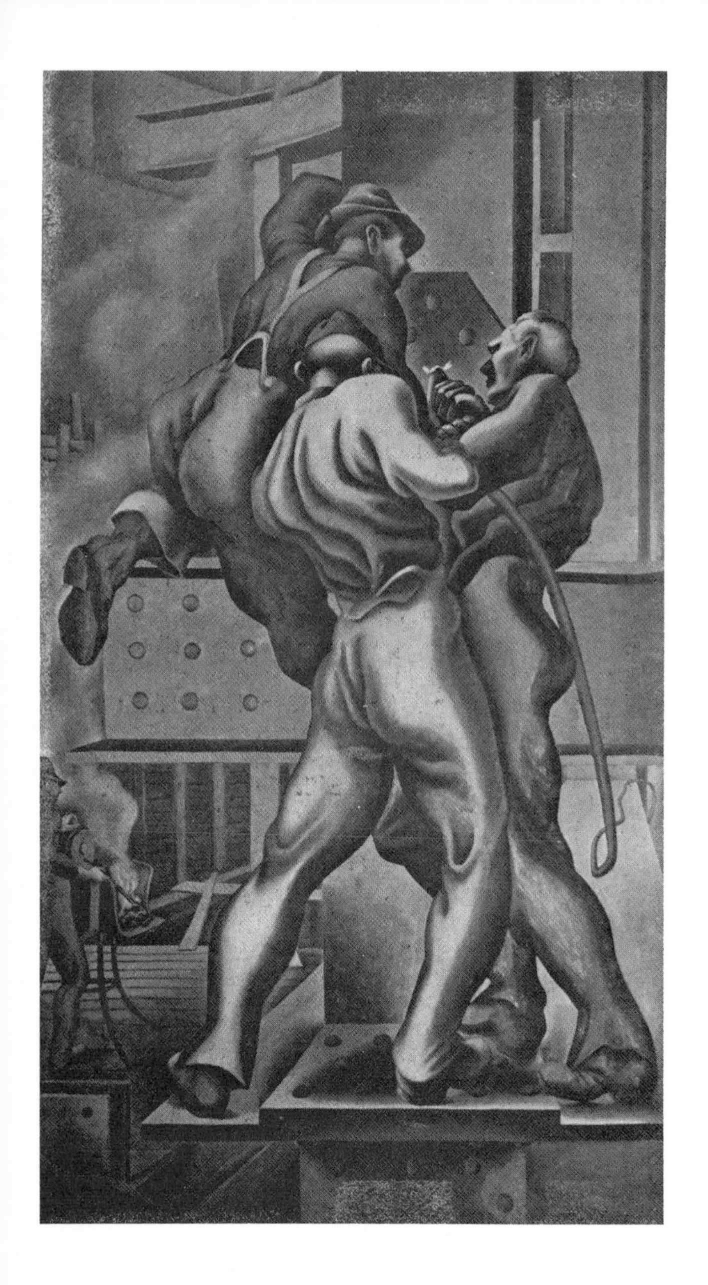

THOMAS

Byron Thomas, painter. Born in Baltimore, Maryland, 1902. Studied at the Art Students' League, 1923-25. Exhibited at the Anderson Gallery with the Tiffany Group, 1929, '30, '31. One-man show at the Ferargil Galleries, 1930. Represented in the Indianapolis Museum.

Large panel (illustrated at left)

Riveting
based on central section of Study

Study for three-part composition (below)

The Excavation and Construction of Radio City

left: Pneumatic Drilling
center: Riveting
right: Excavation

Medium: Oil on canvas.

WATKINS

Franklin Watkins, painter and mural decorator. Born in New York City, 1894. Educated at the University of Virginia, 1911-12, and studied at the Pennsylvania Academy of Fine Arts, 1916-17, '20-'21. One year in Europe on Academy scholarships. Represented in the Pennsylvania Academy of Fine Arts, and the Whitney Museum of American Art. First Prize Carnegie International Exhibition, Pittsburgh, 1931. Murals in the Rodin Museum, Philadelphia.

Large panel (illustrated at right)
based on central section of Study

Study for three-part composition (below)

The Spirit of Man, Crushed by the Machine, Nourishing the Tree of Life

Medium: Oil on canvas.

WOOD

Thomas M. Wood, mural decorator and worker in cut iron. Born in Big Horn, Wyoming, 1903. Studied at the Grand Central School of Art, 1926-27.

Large panel (illustrated at left)
based on left-hand section of Study

Study for three-part composition (below)
Persistence of the West

Medium: Oil on canvas.

PHOTO-MURALS

The photo-murals are designed for a space seven feet high by twelve feet long.

ABBOTT

Photo-Mural

NEW YORK

Technique: "montage," the combining and mounting of sections of different photographs to form one composition; in this mural the photographs of steel girders and plates are mounted in relief

Berenice Abbott, photographer. Born in Springfield, Ohio, 1898. Studied art in Paris and Berlin; photography with Man Ray in Paris. Her work has been included in many European exhibitions of photography. Photographs by her are in the Museum of the City of New York.

BRATTER

Photo-Mural

THREE NEWSPAPER SERVICES
Sports; Financial; Advertising

Maurice Bratter, photographer. Born in Indianapolis, Indiana, 1905. Studied photography with Charles Sheeler since 1928. Exhibited at the Albright Art Gallery, Buffalo, 1932, and the Brooklyn Museum, 1932.

Technique: 3 photographs were selected and copied together to make negative A

Newsprint was photographed for negative B

Positive transparencies were made on A and B which were then superimposed to make a single negative C from which the sketch and panel were enlarged

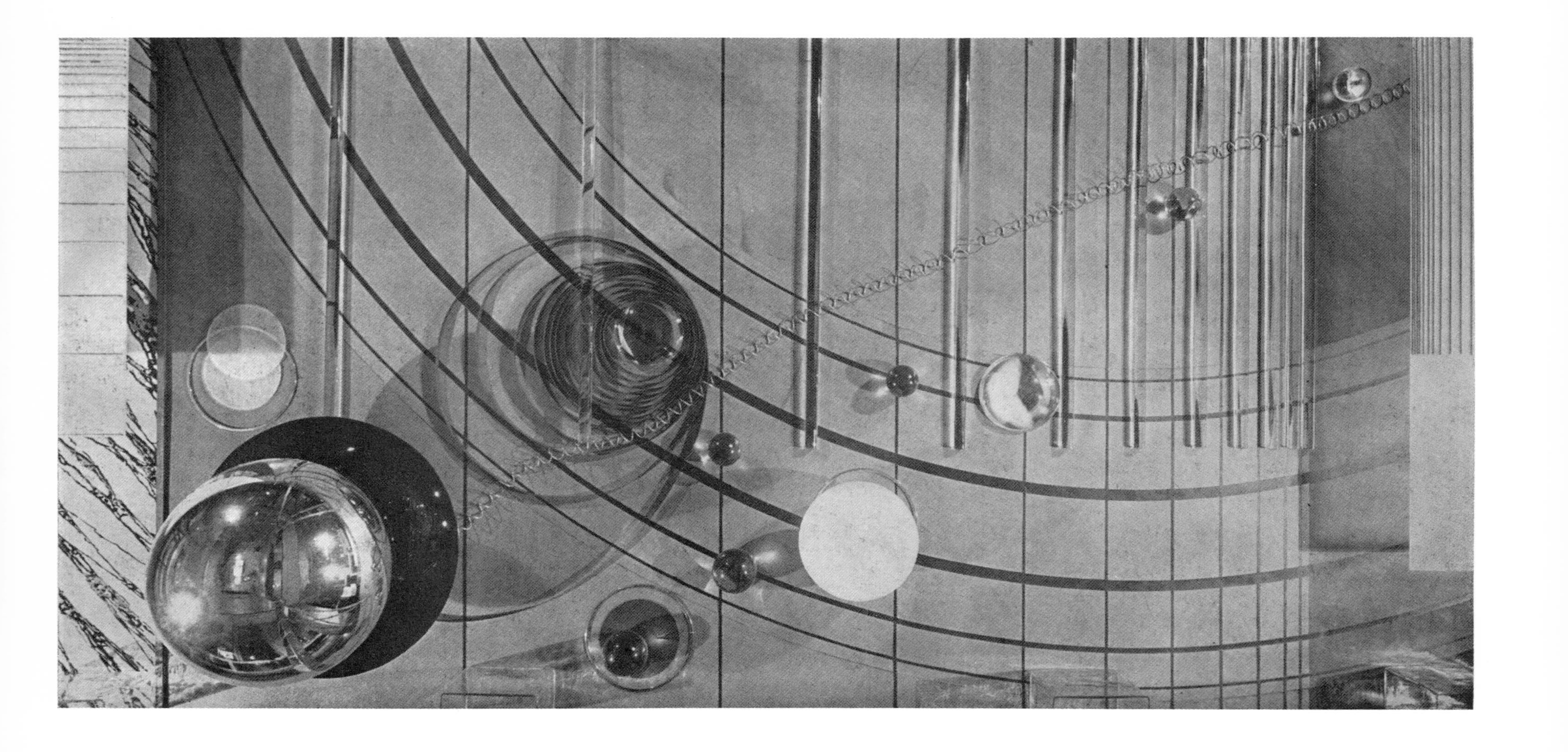

DURYEA AND LOCHER

Photo-Mural

METAL, GLASS, and CORK

Hendrick V. Duryea, photographer. Born in New York City, 1900. Studied photography as an amateur in London. Has been practicing in New York as photographer of architectural subjects since 1920.

Robert E. Locher, architect and mural painter, born in Lancaster, Pennsylvania, 1888. After preparatory school, entered an architect's office as apprentice. Later employed as draughtsman and designer, working on interiors. Came to New York in 1914 to draw and design for periodicals, interior decorators, architects and theatrical producers. Has been practicing since 1920 as decorative painter, interior architect and designer of special installations and accessories.

GERLACH

Photo-Mural
ENERGY

Technique: montage and double printing; negative printing

Arthur Gerlach, photographer. Born in Chicago, Illinois, 1898. Studied sculpture in Italy and later photo-chemistry at Columbia. In 1918 worked with the photographic service in the U. S. Army. His photographs exhibited at the Dudensing Gallery in 1929.

LITTLE AND LEVY

Photo-Mural (Completed too late for illustration)

NEWS

Technique: montage of photographs used for Rotogravure Section of *New York Times*

Emma H. Little: Born in Alexis, Illinois. Educated at Knox College and the University of Illinois. For the last six years in charge of photographic material for the New York *Times*.

Joella Levy: Born in 1907, in Italy, of Italian parents. Educated in Europe.

LYNES

Photo-Mural

AMERICAN LANDSCAPE, 1933

Technique: central panel, photograph framed; side panels, the figures are double-printed from two negatives and mounted on the architectural background

George Platt Lynes, photographer. Born in East Orange, New Jersey, 1907. Has exhibited photographs at the Julien Levy Gallery and at the Leggett Gallery, 1932.

RITTASE

Photo-Mural
STEEL

William M. Rittase, photographer. Born in Baltimore, Maryland, 1894. Studied at the Maryland Art Institute. Was an engineer for ten years and Captain of Artillery during the War. Professional photographer for the last five years.

ROTAN

Photo-Mural
SKYSCRAPERS

Technique: montage of different photographs of the same building

Thurman Rotan, photographer. Born in Waco, Texas, 1903. Studied photography with Ira Martin. His photographic designs were exhibited at the Art Center, 1932.

SHEELER

Photo-Mural
INDUSTRY

Charles Sheeler, photographer and painter. Born in Philadelphia, Pennsylvania, 1883. Studied painting at the Pennsylvania Academy of Fine Arts. Painting first exhibited in the Armory Show, New York, 1913, and since then in many New York galleries. Commenced photographing in 1912. His photographs were exhibited in the important Film and Foto Ausstellung in Stuttgart, 1921, and recently at the Julien Levy Gallery.

SIMON

Photo-Mural

LANDSCAPE AND CITYSCAPE

Stella Simon, photographer. Born in Charleston, South Carolina, 1878. Studied photography with Clarence White. In 1926 completed an experimental cinema film, Ballet of Hands. A series of photographic studies from the League of Composers' production, Oedipus Rex, was exhibited in New York and Philadelphia. An exhibition of her work was held at the Art Center in 1931.

STEICHEN

Photo-Mural (9 feet 10 inches high by 8 feet wide)
GEORGE WASHINGTON BRIDGE

Edward Steichen, photographer and painter. Born, 1879. Educated in Milwaukee, Wisconsin. First photographs, 1896. Commanded photo section, United States Aviation Service, A. E. F., 1918. Gave up painting in 1920. Chief photographer for Condé Nast publications.

SWANK

Photo-Mural

STEEL PLANT

Luke H. Swank. Born at Johnstown, Pennsylvania, 1890. Graduated from the Pennsylvania State College, 1911. Employed as an agricultural expert, cattle breeder, trainer of police dogs, and an employee in father's hardware store until the World War, when he served two years in the Medical Corps and Chemical Warfare Service. Has recently devoted all his time to photography. Exhibited in Brooklyn Museum Exhibition of International Photographers, 1932.

THIS REPRINTED EDITION WAS PRODUCED BY THE OFFSET PRINTING PROCESS. THE TEXT AND PLATES WERE PHOTOGRAPHED SEPARATELY FROM THE ORIGINAL VOLUME, AND THE PLATES RESCREENED. THE PAPER AND BINDING WERE SELECTED TO ENSURE THE LONG LIFE OF THIS LIBRARY GRADE EDITION.

*Two thousand copies of this cata-
log were printed for the Trustees
of the Museum of Modern Art,
by Kaplan & Lapan, Inc.,
New York, May, 1932.*